"YOU HAVE YOUNG ONSET PARKINSONS'."

You Have Young Onset Parkinson's

How I Learned to Live Positively with Early Onset Parkinson's Disease (and How You Will Too)

Blake L. Bookstaff

FOREWORD BY
Willie Geist

LINKED
MIND

CONTENTS

FOREWORD
By Willie Geist

47. It is a number that has hung over me quietly for three decades. My father was 47 years old when he was diagnosed with Parkinson's Disease. As I write this, I am 47 and occasionally wondering if that will be my number too.

For years, our parents did not give a name to my dad's diagnosis —it was always his "neurological thing"—but eventually it hit my sister and me like a thunderbolt that he had Parkinson's. We knew that was a very scary word. It was the disease that Michael J. Fox has. It was also the one with no cure.

But for some 25 years after the initial shock of hearing from a doctor that he had PD, my dad continued to live and work at full speed. Through the small daily struggles and the long list of medications and the surgery, he lived. As I closed in on 47, that gave me hope and inspiration. Even if my number is called, there is life after. Good life.

My dad's doctors say the toxic Agent Orange chemicals he breathed in the jungles of Vietnam slowly and cruelly attacked his nervous system, resulting in Parkinson's Disease. That his PD was not genetic eased my mind, but only slightly. I still thought about 47. I still do.

47 was Blake Bookstaff's number too. And, like my dad, Blake is proving there is life after a Parkinson's diagnosis. The pages that follow will inspire anyone with early onset Parkinson's Disease—and their families—to move forward with the knowledge that there is plenty of good life ahead.

Willie Geist,
Journalist, Anchor of NBC's *Sunday Today with Willie Geist* and Co-Anchor of MSNBC's *Morning Joe*

DEDICATION

I want to thank my doctors for managing my care, the pharmaceutical companies for making the drugs I need to make life with Parkinson's livable, the researchers trying to develop new treatments, and the brave souls participating in clinical trials.

I am grateful to Michael J. Fox for founding such an awesome foundation. I'm also thankful to the National Parkinson's Foundation for their 'Centers for Excellence' designations to help people find care.

I would not and could not have gotten this book written if it hadn't been for Scott Carbonara at Spiritus Communications, who helped me co-write it, along with providing a little therapy on the side; a two-for-one. Scott, thanks for keeping me on task. I appreciate you greatly.

Just because you have the text written doesn't mean you have a "book" ready to publish. Thanks to Paul Hawkins for getting me through this and producing all of the artwork, design and layout (and his wife Linn Hart for the illustrations.) You made this process easy, had great ideas and you were fun to work with.

I never thought I'd say this regarding exercise, but thanks to my trainer Zach Guza of Black Dog Fitness for keeping me strong, as well as making exercise more enjoyable and less routine by always coming up with new things to do.

Rhonda Britt, thanks for all the therapeutic massages, and also thanks for always having a same day appointment available when I am in need.

Shane Cox, thanks for all the stretching and keeping me limber throughout the years with your ninja moves.

Jon Alexander, when I met you fresh off my diagnosis at the World Parkinson's Conference in Overwhelm City, USA, you were a light. I was not in a great way mentally, and you befriending and welcoming me will never be forgotten.

To my business partner and friend Ernie Falco III of ME3 Digital and to my friends Lori Stryer, David Bolinger and the team of RIVR Media, thanks for jumping in and graciously offering to help with parts of the book promotion. Your talents are greatly appreciated.

Thanks to my business partners for the friendship as well as the businesses and opportunities that keep me busy.

Also thanks to my business partner and friend Robert Hart, who is always willing to help me with about anything on a moment's notice.

To one of my best friends, Bryce, thanks for keeping my secret early on as well as reading my early text rants.

I have the best family in the world. Really. If they gave out lottery tickets for families, I certainly would have won the grand prize. Thanks Mom and Dad for always being there for me. And to my sister, Jessica, you are awesome and the best sister a brother could ask for.

To my wife, Jennifer, I love you more than words can describe. Thanks for staying positive and helping to ensure that Parkinson's does not define me.

And to Eleanor, our daughter, you are spectacular and by far my life's greatest accomplishment—followed closely by me getting your mom to marry me!

I dedicate this book to you.

DISCLAIMER

Do you remember the line from the 1980s Vicks Formula 44 cough syrup commercial, "I'm not a doctor, but I play one on TV"?

Let me share this right up front: *I am neither a doctor, nor have I played one on TV*.

What I am is an entrepreneur, husband, father, son, brother, and friend who happened to be diagnosed with young onset Parkinson's disease.

This book is not intended to provide medical advice, diagnosis, or treatment for Parkinson's—or any other disease you might have. Instead, this book is about my journey with young onset Parkinson's. I wrote it to offer hope and insight from the perspective of one who has walked this path. I recognize that not all cases of Parkinson's disease are the same. People also have different life situations than me.

References to my own medical regime and treatment are included as biographical aspects of my own experience, and are included for educational and informational purposes only. Doctors' names have been changed to preserve their privacy.

— Blake L. Bookstaff

"I AM A LUCKY GUY..."

Introduction

This book is primarily for those newly diagnosed with young onset Parkinson's disease, as well as their families and friends who might want to better understand what their loved ones are going through.

When I was diagnosed with young onset Parkinson's disease (also referred to as early onset Parkinson's disease) at age forty-seven, I didn't know what to do. I was beyond devastated. In my search to get help, I read books and looked for a community of others like me. In that search, I discovered there really were no people to talk to or resources geared to the younger diagnosed person, because this diagnosis represents such a minority of overall cases.

I mean, there were support groups for those with Parkinson's disease, but usually meetings were held in a senior center, and it seemed the average age of those attending was eighty.

What I'm about to say shouldn't be taken as a slight to older people with Parkinson's; but a person who has been diagnosed at a younger age doesn't want to see older people diagnosed in walkers and with canes. They want to see people like them who are still active—hiking, traveling, and enjoying life. Those images and examples are what motivate them.

That void in providing the right type of support to those diagnosed at a young age was the impetus for me sharing my story.

I'm one lucky guy. I'm the guy who pulls up to the full parking lot to find the driver backing out of a front row space. From having my business partners and a great family, to enjoying my work and having that work be profitable—I'm truly blessed.

When I think about how my life has gone—the sequence of events, good and bad, that needed to happen for me to end up here—I'm truly amazed.

For example, I read a newspaper article when I was in college. I called up the person who was featured in the article and ended up becoming his business partner. Several years later, that business got me into another business. One day, we had a pressing matter that needed to be dealt with, and our lawyer had to leave town. He introduced me to his lawyer colleague and said she would need to handle the matter. That newly assigned lawyer later became my wife. Later, our daughter came into the world. I'm shortening things up in this sequence of events, but the point is that all the little steps—everything that happened and the order in which they happened—needed to take place in a certain way to bring me where I am today. If I hadn't read that article in the local newspaper many years ago, I wouldn't have had the business, wouldn't have needed an attorney to deal with a legal issue, and wouldn't now be married to Jennifer or have Eleanor.

I have countless examples like this, all of which make me believe that there is a purpose in everything that happens, even if something might not seem so fortunate at the time.

I'm not yet sure of the greater point within my Parkinson's journey, but I'm sure that there is one, and that it will be revealed to me someday.

"YOU HAVE YOUNG ONSET PARKINSON'S."

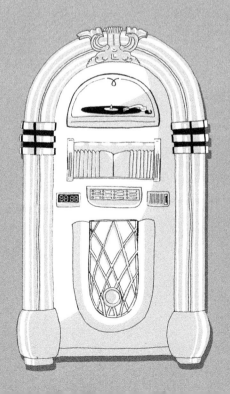

Chapter 1

Five Little Words

I've had a great life, filled with many unique experiences and blessings.

At an early age, my parents instilled me with their work ethic. Since my father owned a large restaurant and bar, he had me working in the family business as early as I can remember. At nine, I was running the cash register, taking money from customers who were paying their bills. I loved counting money and running the credit cards. I was too short for the job, but that was nothing a stool couldn't fix. Customers didn't always know how to deal with my young age. Some were amused, some were impressed, and some kept looking around—waiting for an adult to come over to help them.

Dad treated me as an adult and let me do adult jobs. I sold T-shirts, ran a waiting list of a hundred people on busy Saturday nights, showed people to their tables, worked in the kitchen, restocked the salad bar, and washed dishes, to name a few tasks. Some Saturdays we would not get home until midnight.

By the time I turned eleven, I'd head to work straight after school—which was about a block away—to restock the automatic bar system with bottles of liquor. That's some trust my dad had in me right there.

I always loved buttons and switches, anything mechanical or electronic. That's probably what drew me to the arcade next door. (That, along with gambling on video games with the restaurant employees, but that's another story...) After finishing work at the restaurant, I started heading over to the arcade. Before long, I noticed they were selling a jukebox.

"Dad," I said excitedly over dinner one night, "With my money, I can buy a used jukebox. Will you let me put it in the bar? I think it'll make money. What do you think?"

"Sounds like a great idea," my dad responded, always eager to support my endeavors.

I'll never forget the feeling I had the first time I "robbed" (took the money out of) the jukebox. Loads of beautiful quarters slid around the metal coin box, making music as I lifted and dropped them into my cash bag. As I rolled the money (taking the coins and putting them in paper wrappers so the bank would take them) before depositing it, I realized I also loved the instant feedback that *my idea had worked.* This fueled my interest in starting my own entrepreneurial ventures—which is a good thing, since I never got an offer on any job I interviewed for, including for a restaurant server position! Imagine the different path my life could have taken if they'd hired me. I owe them a big thanks.

Life is full of chapters—some that run concurrently and others that don't. Some are great, others are not.

Fast forward many years, my business career was successful and going full steam ahead. My personal life, well, it needed some work. But that all changed one day when luck intervened. On a day that I needed something quickly, my regular lawyer was tied up out of town, so he told me that his associate, Jennifer, would help me instead. While I thought our meeting went great, I later learned that immediately after I left her office, she called her friend to complain about *this tool* she'd just met. Yeah, that would be me. A few years later, somehow this beautiful lady—with the prettiest blue eyes I'd ever seen— became my bride.

Skip ahead in time a bit, and I was helping choose baby names. Shortly thereafter, at an out-of-town hospital on Christmas Eve, a doctor asked me if I wanted to hold my precious baby daughter for the first time. My heart skipped a beat, as my eyes fell on our little treasure. I recall thinking, "I can't believe she's mine." Our lives went from zero to a hundred in one night with this little person to care for 24/7. I thought I was ready, but I wasn't.

In thinking about this book, I originally thought it could be interesting to outline different life-altering events and give each its own section, all with a five-word title. Some I came up with, as cheesy as they might be, were:

"Working in the family business."

"The making of an entrepreneur."

"You may kiss the bride."

"You can hold your baby."

Life offers us fantastic experiences, but it can deliver devastating ones, too. A few short years later, my neurologist uttered his own five little words. They reached my ears, but somehow my brain refused to process them. When I finally regained focus, I heard what she had said. Five little words that would forever change my life, landing in my brain like a bomb.

"You have young onset Parkinson's."

KABOOM!

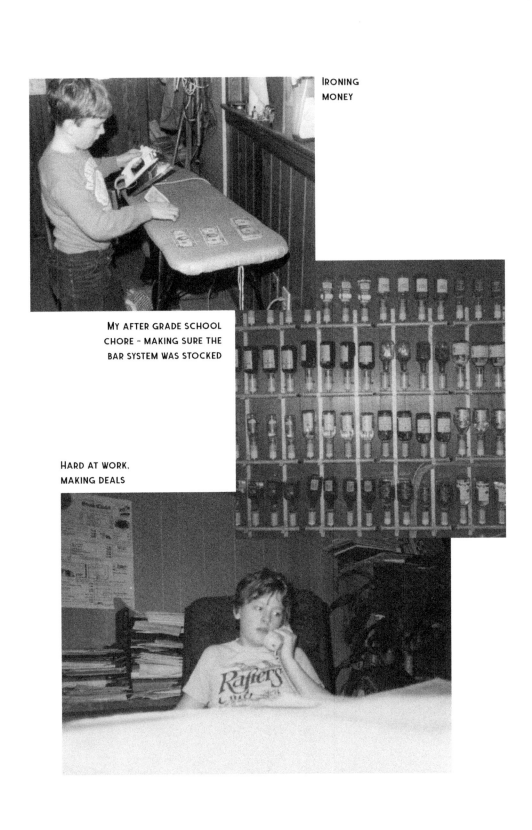

IRONING
MONEY

MY AFTER GRADE SCHOOL
CHORE - MAKING SURE THE
BAR SYSTEM WAS STOCKED

HARD AT WORK.
MAKING DEALS

TENDING THE GRILL AT UNCLE BLAKE'S BBQ

MY BEAUTIFUL BRIDE JENNIFER

THE FIRST TIME I GOT TO HOLD ELEANOR

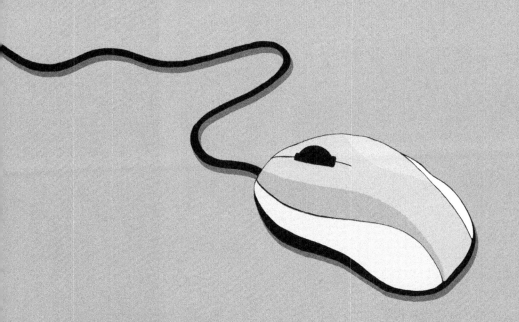

Chapter 2

Am I Just Getting Old?

I'd always been full of energy and able to juggle multiple ideas, work tasks, friendships, and family. I chalked it up to good genes and large amounts of Diet Coke.

At age thirty, I felt like I was twenty. At forty, I felt like I was thirty. My body still felt youthful, and my mind stayed sharp. I thought I was in great shape for my age.

As I entered my mid-forties, my, how things changed.

One afternoon at age forty-five, I jumped on my exercise bike for my afternoon workout routine while thinking about all the things I wanted to get done the next day. After a few minutes of riding, the toes on my right foot curled up on the pedal, almost like an involuntary cramp or contraction coming from the arch of my foot. I didn't know if I had a problem with a tendon, muscle, or bone, but it felt like my foot got bound up with a rubber band. I had to stop riding for a second to let it loosen up so I could continue my workout.

I didn't think anything of it, even though it went on for months. It seemed like around minute five of my workouts, my toes would trigger. I'd have to move my foot to a different angle or position of the pedal to keep it from happening again. It was an annoyance, and when the cramping got worse and more frequent, I told my wife about it.

"Maybe you should see your doctor," Jennifer suggested in October of 2014. "Make sure you haven't injured it. Your workouts could be making it worse."

My internist referred me to a podiatrist who told me I had plantar fasciitis, although it wasn't a typical presentation. She believed the same treatment would work, and referred me to physical therapy. After several visits with the therapist, I got better. Well, not completely better, but I felt good enough to continue my afternoon workouts.

Then in March of 2015, I stretched my hands towards the ceiling like I usually did while waking up in bed. As I put my arms down to the bed, I noticed my right hand was very choppy going down, almost as if it were on a gear that had a ratchet. After one cycle of this, it would go down as smoothly as my left hand—until the next day, when it would happen again. It wasn't painful—it was just weird.

In hindsight, I'm not sure why I let these problems go on for so long. Have you ever driven while looking through a dirty windshield? Maybe when the first few bugs hit the glass, it gets your attention. But after a while, you get used to the view. When you try to clean the windshield with your wipers, you don't even notice the streaks left behind. After a while, you get used to looking past the haze.

That's how I felt about my hand. At first, I just accepted it as my new normal. Then it got worse, to the point where I couldn't raise my arm above the level of my shoulder. That's when I went back to the doctor—and, drum roll please, more physical therapy.

Fortunately, the physical therapist my doctor sent me to knew exactly what he was looking at.

"It's a frozen shoulder," he said after testing my range of motion.

"You're sure?" I wanted to know.

"I wrote my master's thesis on the subject," he nodded confidently.

I'm glad this guy knows his stuff, I thought as I began PT. *If anyone can help me, it's this therapist.*

By August of that same year, the pain in my shoulder still bothered me enough to see a local orthopedist. He thought I had a problem with inflammation in the joint, and he gave me a steroid pack. Between PT and the steroids, I got better, like ninety-five percent better!

Thank goodness that's behind me, I thought after my last visit to the PT.

Unknown to me, not long after I completed PT for my shoulder, my niece, Harper, watched me reaching to change the radio station in the car. She asked my wife, "Why is Blake moving like an old man?" Whatever was going on in my body, it had happened over time. I compared how I felt one day based on how I felt the day before. Maybe I was walking more slowly and cautiously than I used to. But as far as I was concerned, each day kept getting better.

When my foot gave me problems, I got help until it felt better. Then when my shoulder froze up, I got it sorted out through physical therapy. I figured this was the normal aging process. I'd never been in my forties before. I used to hear people talk about being over forty. They called it "over the hill" and shared stories about their aches and pains. I'd never been this age before. *Maybe this is normal and how I'm supposed to feel,* I told myself. *Perhaps this is what getting older means.* I accepted that things that had never acted up before were going to act up from time to time. *But it's not a big deal,* I reassured myself. *You go to the doctor; you get physical therapy; and you bounce back as good as new, or like 95 percent as good as new.*

I threw myself back into work, where I spent a lot of time on the computer. In October of 2015, my index finger occasionally started clicking the mouse button on its own. It didn't happen all the time, but it started firing involuntarily. I shot a video of my finger, thinking I could show my doctor the problem instead of just trying to describe it. I wasn't super-worried and didn't think much about it, really.

This has got to be related to my shoulder problem, I told myself. *It's on the same side of my body. I must have pinched something that's still getting worked out as I heal.*

I never thought of myself as a hypochondriac, even though one friend teased me about going to the doctor as often as I did. After a bout with chest pain, I thought I might be having a heart attack. *But it's normal to have something like that checked out, right?* I told myself. It turned out that my heart was fine, which was good—but I had to know more. I bought a heart rate sensor on Amazon. Turns out, my heart really was fine.

Maybe I obsessed about my health too much; who knows? I was (and am) certainly on a first-name basis with the office staff at my internist's office.

In mid-November of 2015, I made an appointment with my internist, Dr. Hart, to discuss the auto-firing index finger on my right hand. I needed to get this under control so that I wouldn't have a bunch of unintended Amazon purchases. In all seriousness, I showed her the video of my twitching. Then we reviewed my recent history with foot and shoulder problems. Then, she commented on my slightly shaky hands—which I'd had most of my life. I always attributed it to the caffeine I drank.

"One of my friends calls me Shaky Blake," I joked. "I drink a lot of Diet Coke."

After she conducted a thorough exam, she made some notes on her computer before turning back to me.

"Let me say up front that I *don't* think you have Parkinson's," Dr. Hart said as a disclaimer. "I've got five other patients with that disease, but of course, all of them are quite a bit older than you. I work closely with a neurologist in Knoxville. Let me get you an appointment with him, so we can completely rule out anything major."

Within a couple of weeks, I saw her neurologist contact in Knoxville. My first thought when I walked through the door was *this place is a shit box.* I'm sure that my impression had something to do with my feeling unsettled about being at the neurologist's office in the first place. Still, I couldn't shake that bad feeling inside of me.

I found the doctor pleasant enough. Because of the visits I'd had with my own doctor about my foot, shoulder, and finger issues, I probably could have gone through the complete neurological examination without him telling me what to do next. Just the same, he put me through the usual tests. Finally, he had me walk up and down the hall while he watched.

"You don't swing your right arm when you walk," the doctor observed.

"You mean like the lady in the *Seinfeld* episode that didn't swing her arms when she walked?" I joked with him, as I did my best to imitate her walk—prancing around, holding my hands out to the side while carrying invisible suitcases like she had on the show. I chuckled as I acted.

Apparently, he'd not seen the show and didn't get my joke—or didn't find it as amusing as I had.

He did, though, offer two things. First, he gave me some medical patches to try, something called NEUPRO®. Second, he scheduled me for something called a DaTscan the next morning. He handed me a brochure which explained the test.

"And let me say," he assured me as I left his office, "I don't think you have Parkinson's. You don't present with typical Parkinson's symptoms. Wear the NEUPRO® patch, get in for your DaTscan, and then we'll talk once I get the results."

Reading through the brochure and his notes while waiting to pay, my eyes fell on something he wrote at the bottom of my form: *possible Parkinson's diagnosis.*

I never thought about how the various symptoms in my body might be connected until I read those words. I kept assuming the problems I had were unrelated, except that my twitching finger could be connected to my frozen shoulder. *A pinched nerve at the shoulder could show up in my finger, right? Then how could my first problem—contractions in my right foot—relate to something from my shoulder area? And why are my problems all on the right side of my body?* I wondered.

But a *possible Parkinson's diagnosis?* That really freaked me out, and my hands trembled even more as I got to my car.

Back home, I read up on the DaTscan. I learned the test is invasive, involving a radioactive dye injection. Then I read if they didn't do it just right, I could end up with organ damage. The test measures dopamine in the brain, and from the little reading I'd done, I knew that people suffering with Parkinson's have low dopamine levels. While I know that I talked to my wife about the visit with the neurologist and the DaTscan, I don't remember the conversation. I became so preoccupied with concern that part of me was operating on autopilot.

I called my internist, Dr. Hart, that night.

"He wants to test me for Parkinson's," I told her. I tried to sound calm, while obviously being unsettled.

"Let me call him, then I'll call you back," she offered.

"Look, his office was depressing, and that whole experience has me troubled," I told her. "I don't want to go back to him. If you even slightly think I have Parkinson's, send me to someone who specializes in this disease, so we can rule it out."

Dr. Hart called the neurologist I'd seen. Then, as promised, she called me back. She spent more than an hour on the phone with me. The short version is that she assured me that the DaTscan test was fairly routine, as well as rarely problematic.

"But," she suggested, "if you don't want to undergo that test, you should go to Vanderbilt where they have neurologists specializing in Parkinson's. Movement disorder specialists have more experience in diagnosing complicated neurological issues than general neurologists."

Unfortunately, these specialists get booked nine to eighteen months out. Fortunately, they open a few slots from time to time.

Dr. Hart got me one of those open slots two months later—with Dr. Morris at Vanderbilt University Medical Center in Nashville, Tennessee, a neurologist specializing in movement disorders. Since Vanderbilt was a few hours away, my wife and I decided to make an overnight trip of it and have some fun. The morning of my appointment, we tossed an overnight bag in the car, drove to Nashville, and headed to the medical center.

Dr. Morris had already reviewed my records before my appointment. After she entered the room and made introductions, she put me through another battery of physical exams. She tested my grip, range of motion, reflexes, coordination, memory, and watched me walk down the hall. At some point, Dr. Morris mentioned that she'd spent time in Colorado. That fact stuck with me, since we have spent some time in Colorado as well.

The doctor left the room, and my wife and I settled back in our chairs, not sure what to expect next. After a few minutes, she came back into the room and began talking in an upbeat voice.

"So," the doctor said, "we're going to try you out on this medication for two weeks. Then," she kept talking about something, but my mind got hung up on something that she'd said a moment before. Or maybe something she didn't say earlier. Either way, when my focus returned, I felt like I'd just walked into the middle of a movie, unsure of what had happened in the previous scene.

"Whoa. Wait a minute," I said, raising my head and looking her in the eye. "Are you saying I have Parkinson's?"

"I think you do, yes," she said in her very chill, soft-spoken way. "Specifically, I believe you have young onset Parkinson's."

After that moment, she sounded to me like Charlie Brown's mother. *Wah-wah wah wah-wah wah whah wah whahwa* was all I heard come from her mouth.

"So, the medicine?" Jennifer started to ask.

"The medicine works to alleviate the symptoms of Parkinson's, and we also use it as a diagnostic tool," the doctor explained. Then turning back to me, she said, "If you're *lucky*, you will feel this medicine helps your symptoms, which will be another indicator you have Parkinson's. I say lucky, because with Parkinson's, you have treatment options and medicines that will help. If the medicine doesn't work, it's not Parkinson's, and we might not have treatment options for you. There are some conditions we cannot treat."

Again, I heard, *Wah-wah wah wah-wah whahwa.*

I tried to ask a few questions, uttering some crackling words out of my mouth, but I was unsuccessful. Emotions flooded my body, and all I could do was produce tears. I could not talk anymore; I was *done.*

My wife turned to me.

"Blake, why don't you step outside?" she offered. "I'll handle the rest of the appointment." I walked out of the room—stunned and overwhelmed, as if someone had tossed a flash grenade at my feet.

I went into the hallway and just leaned against a vending machine teary-eyed, waiting for Jennifer to finish up with the doctor and check-out. My mind was running a million miles a minute but starting to shut down at the same time. I just couldn't believe it. *I'm going to take some pills, and if I am "lucky," the pills will work, confirming the Parkinson's diagnosis.* I kept playing the tape of the neurologist's monologue in my head.

I didn't know much, but I knew one thing: I didn't feel *lucky. Devastated*, yes. But lucky? Not at all.

"I JUST CAN'T BELIEVE IT..."

CHAPTER 3

DENIAL

To say I got trapped inside my head at that moment would be an understatement. When doctors talk about someone being in shock, they mean a medical condition—like what happens with trauma, blood loss, heatstroke, infection, or poisoning. The kind of trauma I felt originated in my mind, but it manifested in my body. My anxiety spiked through the roof—making my heart pound and my breathing shallow. *How could this be?*

The night before, while playing pinball with Bryce, I mentioned that Jennifer and I were heading to Nashville for an overnight.

"What're you doing in Nashville?" Bryce asked.

"Hopefully the same thing I'm doing now. Playing a few games and having a couple of drinks," I joked with him. "But, uh," I added, "I'm going to see a doctor at Vanderbilt."

I told Bryce about some of the things I'd had going on in my body, while he listened quietly. When I finished, he gave me his thoughts.

"Parkinson's?" he smiled. "Isn't that, you know...?" he started to say.

"Yeah, it's an old person's disease," I finished his sentence.

The two of us laughed about it, and then went back to our game. *Parkinson's? I thought. Ridiculous!*

I wasn't laughing now. Instead, I was trying to hold back tears, as I waited for Jennifer to join me after finishing her private discussion with the doctor.

We walked to the entrance of the medical center, and I waited as she pulled the car around.

When I got in the car, Jennifer filled me in on the rest of what she'd learned from Dr. Morris, and when I'd have my next appointment. All I could mutter in between tears was, "I just can't believe it. I just can't believe it. I just can't believe it."

Jennifer assured me that we'd *get through this.*

We'd planned to enjoy Franklin, Tennessee, that night—checking out a few bars and maybe catching some live music. I wouldn't have made those plans if I'd thought this doctor's visit would be anything other than routine.

"So I'm just supposed to take the medicine?" I asked Jennifer as we drove to the hotel. "If I feel better, I have Parkinson's? Did I hear that right?"

Jennifer nodded.

I didn't know if I should hope the medicine would work, confirming Parkinson's, or if I should cross my fingers that the medicine did nothing, leaving me undiagnosed and perhaps untreatable. I was hoping I would wake up and realize this was all just a bad dream.

Despite the anxiety-producing news, we decided to stay the night and make the best of our time in Franklin instead of cutting our trip short. But from the time I left the hospital until we got to the hotel, I sobbed. To put it bluntly, I was just *so sad*.

Jennifer tried to cheer me up by taking me to the hotel bar before we headed into town for the night. I didn't try to outrun or even outdrink the topic weighing on my mind.

If you've ever tried pushing something out of your mind, you know it's futile. Attempting to shove thoughts aside just brings them closer, especially with my hyper-focused mind that is always thinking about something.

Our first stop was the hotel lobby bar. Jennifer and I did our best to stay in the moment and enjoy our drinks.

Then the phone rang. Bryce came up on my screen.

"Hello?" I answered.

"Hey, Blake," Bryce said lightly. "I was thinking about you. How did things go today?"

I told him what we'd learned, trying unsuccessfully to hold back my emotions.

After a couple of minutes, I told Bryce that I couldn't talk about it any longer. We hung up and said we would talk later.

That call would lead to more tears.

Later, I felt badly for how quickly I got off the phone with Bryce, so I texted him:

> I really appreciate you calling, Bryce. That means a lot to me. Jennifer has been great, although I am extremely devastated at the moment. Been crying a lot to myself. Too raw right now. Had to take a Xanax. Can't really believe it. Will have to change my attitude about it.

Bryce didn't take long to respond:

> Life sure seems a lot sweeter and
> precious for me tonight. I don't
> always appreciate it fully. I just
> walked around the grocery store in a
> surreal state of mind, then bawled my
> eyes out at home. Emotional news for
> me. More upsides to follow.

Not all of the tears shed that night were mine. Bryce knew I was devastated, and he hurt for me.

I hurt for me, too. I cried a lot from my appointment to the time we checked into the hotel. And I cried more over drinks that night. I was a faucet. Not a hysterical faucet—just a sad, constant, dripping spigot. In between bouts of tears, my wife and I talked, but my mind kept drifting elsewhere.

This has got to be a mistake, I told myself over and over, whenever the doctor's words echoed in my head saying, "You have young onset Parkinson's." *How long is this charade going to last?*

I'd had a little experience dealing with surprising, even traumatic events. Years before, Jennifer and I had taken a "quick overnight trip" to Bowling Green, Kentucky, flying on a small plane to visit my wife's mom for Christmas when Jennifer was seven months pregnant. *No problem,* though, according to our doctor. We were told that she could fly until the end of December. We were flying a week before the cut-off, so all should have been fine.

But we experienced turbulence on the flight. I've flown a ton. Jumbo jets, little propeller planes, and everything in between. This was up there as one of the bumpiest flights I'd ever been on, and that's saying a lot. My normally stoic wife shed tears.

Long story short, the turbulence rocked the plane so much, it induced her labor. Shortly after landing, we found ourselves in an operating room at a relatively small hospital during the Christmas holiday. Did I mention it was December 24? We'd flown into Bowling Green to have Christmas Eve Dinner with my wife's family, and instead we had a baby—our precious Eleanor. We anticipated a brief overnight stay and Christmas Eve dinner with my in-laws, but we ended up living in a hotel for weeks with Eleanor in the NICU until she was well enough to travel.

Throughout that entire period, I found myself running on adrenaline and the occasional Xanax to deal with the stress of extreme turbulence, fear for my wife and daughter, being hours from home, and then, once we got home, wondering how in the world I would handle parenting a baby born two months premature without a team of helpers.

But this diagnosis—*You have young onset Parkinson's*—didn't cause my body to respond with adrenaline. It caused me to shut down.

After my call with Bryce, I decided not to tell anyone right away about my diagnosis. I barely kept myself from breaking down when I told Bryce about my disease. I knew that if I started talking about it again, I would cry. In fact, it would be some time before I could talk about it without crying. So that night, Jennifer and I decided we wouldn't tell anyone. Once the genie was out of the bottle, it would be out of the bottle. I needed to keep it contained, as I was still processing this diagnosis.

Once we got home and saw my daughter again, a new, stronger wave of grief washed over me. I couldn't even start to process talking to her about it. *What would I say?*

In the days to come, I felt like I'd lost a loved one, and that loved one was me. I was catatonic. *Why me?* I would later learn that there is something called the five stages of grief, some of which people go through when experiencing loss or a major, unexpected change. Stages one can go through are denial, anger, bargaining, depression, and acceptance. Looking back at this time, I was mainly cycling between depression and denial. Any given day, I hopped around between nearly all those feelings in no particular order.

One would think that once a person reached acceptance, they'd be done. That wasn't the case for me. I could accept parts of my diagnosis, but then slide back into depression for days at a time. Even today, as I consider myself in acceptance of my disease, I still sometimes grieve over the loss of feeling young and somewhat invincible.

Instead of pushing these thoughts away, my mind was constantly computing something new to obsess over. *It must be a mistake. I need to go to another doctor who will straighten this out, confirm the misdiagnosis, and then share a good laugh about this.* I was in disbelief that I had Parkinson's. I did not think of it as denial, but it clearly was, as I was living in a fantasyland.

Denial kept me from taking the medicine Dr. Morris prescribed me. For a month, I let the medicine sit in a drawer, because I didn't even want to look at it or think about it, much less take it. Plus, what if I was wrong and had to take these pills for the rest of my life? There was a part of me that did not want to know.

I did not call my denial *denial*. I thought of it as more of a diversion. Staying busy at work became a nice distraction for me, keeping the mental chatter focused on business for some of the day. Luckily for me, I loved my work. I never viewed work as a job, so I never understood people who dreaded getting up on Monday mornings. Even today, I can't wait to start work each day. It's my creative outlet. Immersing myself in it more during this period was very helpful and therapeutic for me.

As ridiculous as it might sound, buying a Tesla was another distraction. I've always liked technology, so that certainly had a lot to do with my joy over this decision. But this car kept me distracted, in a good way, from facing my Parkinson's diagnosis all at once. It was something to get excited about. Of all the decisions I made in the year after my diagnosis, I'd put the Tesla as one of my best decisions. I'll explain more about why later.

The stages of grief I read about told me I should expect to enter a period of anger. But I'd never been an angry person, and learning I had Parkinson's didn't change that.

I thought that might be another inaccuracy in the model, since I didn't experience anger in my grief. But anger isn't always a screaming, raging tantrum at others. Sometimes, anger goes inwards.

After I thought about it, I realized that I'd turned my anger inside. I couldn't let go of one burning question: *Did I do this to myself? Did I somehow give myself Parkinson's?*

Other than beat myself up mentally about it, I wasn't sure what I'd do even if I could solve the puzzle of *what gave me Parkinson's*. Still, I had a burning desire to know. So I analyzed all of the possibilities.

I grew up on rural well water. I later learned that drinking water from private wells might have increased my likelihood to develop Parkinson's.

Living near fields sprayed with insecticides and herbicides such as Paraquat might also increase the risk of Parkinson's, since those chemicals are often sprayed on farmland and can seep into the water. Fortunately, I hadn't lived near farmland. But I had been around *pesticides*. Chemicals used in pesticides are believed to be a potential environmental risk factor, increasing the risk of developing Parkinson's.

I'd spent years in restaurants that sprayed regularly to keep the bugs out. On top of that, I used an exterminator around my own house who did a lot of inside spraying—something they don't do much anymore.

There was also a study I had recently learned about that suggested drinking soft drinks, either with sugar or artificial sweeteners, increased the risk of developing Parkinson's. Did I mention that I drink Diet Coke all day long? Drinking from plastic and Styrofoam cups could be another culprit that increases Parkinson's risk. Guess what I drink my Diet Coke from? Plastic and Styrofoam cups full of ice.

Did I give myself Parkinson's?

There's even a study that suggests people suffering with allergic rhinitis, what we call "hay fever," are more susceptible to Parkinson's. I've gotten monthly allergy shots for hay fever for twenty years.

As I kept looking for the cause of my illness, I also found another possible answer: genetics. I'd learn more about that later.

They say about Parkinson's that "genetics load the gun; environment pulls the trigger." In my quest to find out what did this, an impossible thing to confirm, I reached my lowest stage— the one called depression.

"I FOUND THE RIGHT WORD..."

CHAPTER 4

HEARTBROKEN

I'M A HAPPY GUY. I'VE ALWAYS HAD A POSITIVE ATTITUDE about life, and those who know me well can tell you that I'm not the sort of person to get down and stay down.

But I had a lot to learn about depression.

Some people, of course, suffer from chronic depression. From what I understand, people with chronic depression live with constant down moods and lose interest in activities that would normally cause happiness. Chronic depression, I have read, probably comes from emotional, genetic, or social causes that can mess with a person's sleep, appetite, focus, energy, and routines. And it can lead to suicidal thoughts.

I thank God that I've never suffered from chronic depression, and my heart goes out to those living with it. By nature, I'm almost the opposite of depressed. I've always been quick to joke and just as quick to laugh. I've had a terrific life—great parents and family, unbelievable experiences, jobs I love, a beautiful and supportive wife, amazing friends, and the most perfect daughter—which have always given me a sense of gratitude and happiness.

What I had now, though, was a type of depression that comes with grief.

I've always written down ideas and thoughts since I was a teenager. It's not like I write "Dear Diary," share my innermost secrets, and then lock it up afterwards. But rather, it's a way to capture a thought or idea so I won't lose it. I heard too many people talk about great ideas that came to them in a dream or in the shower, but they forgot those ideas minutes later, because they didn't write them down. As an entrepreneur, I always have ideas popping into my head, some better than others. But if I don't record them, I lose them.

After my diagnosis, one of the first things I did was to start writing down different thoughts about my feelings. I was very depressed and so overwhelmed that journaling my thoughts became an initial form of therapy for me. It was certainly better than talking about it, which would bring me to tears every time.

I wanted to identify the right word to describe what I felt when I first heard the diagnosis. I could not figure it out for quite a while. *Was I sad?* Yes, of course. *Disappointed?* Yes. *Scared?* Yes, too. My brainstorming went on and on, but none of the words really worked, because they didn't go far enough to describe my feelings.

It took me months to think of the right word that truly summed up how I felt. Then I came up with it: *heartbroken.*

That word spoke to the heart of my emotions. When I thought about having Parkinson's, I was heartbroken. I had to let go of my picture of how I imagined my life would be. Whenever I'd thought about my future before, the possibility of Parkinson's had never entered my mind. But now, I couldn't get Parkinson's out of my head.

After three or four weeks of struggling to wrap my head around my diagnosis, I don't think anyone outside of my immediate household would have known I was battling depression. I'm not sure my wife even knew how blue I felt about this "gift" of a diagnosis. Work became my distraction and escape, which I found easy since I've always loved work.

My work requires me to really think and focus to get things done. If my work were more routine, I'd have too many brain cells left to invest in worrying.

I'm a serial entrepreneur. That means my mind lives in a state of controlled chaos, one that involves constant distraction and multitasking to get things done. Because of my nature and experience, I was always ready to get pulled in different directions on short notice to respond to any crisis or opportunity that came up. But having Parkinson's added another distraction, a bad one: medication.

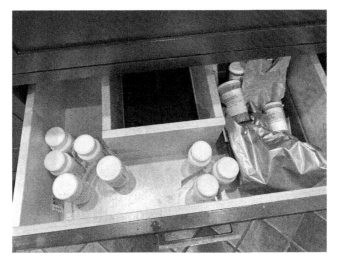

The pharmacy

Eventually, I started taking those pills. Three times each day, I had to pull out my contact case of pills I kept in my pocket. No matter what I was doing or what was going on around me, those pills, and that schedule, kept my mind chained to my disease.

I could be engaged in my favorite, most exciting type of work, but then it would be time to take my pills. Even before I reached into my pocket to pull out my medicine, my mind went off track and told me, *You've got Parkinson's*, like an evil version of the old AOL slogan, *You've got mail.* Those pills had the power to take me out of a state of happy distraction and pull my mind back into the place I tried to avoid: *You've got Parkinson's.*

For a long time, just taking my medicine set off a chain reaction of negative thoughts inside me. Each time I had to take my pills, it reminded me that I would be taking these pills—and probably many more pills just like these—for the rest of my life. I knew that over time, the medicine would become less and less effective. And I understood that the ten hours of work I crammed into eight hours each day wouldn't last either. Eventually, I'd work eight hours to produce eight hours of results. Then those same eight hours would produce six hours of results. Then four. Then two. Then I'd be disabled.

Those weren't the only thoughts I had to fight against. I knew it wouldn't be long before I could no longer do the things I'd always enjoyed most, like snow skiing and travel. I realized that once I could no longer hide my symptoms, some of my business associates wouldn't want to partner with me, fearing that I would become completely disabled or drop dead in the middle of a project. Then I started thinking that I might not be able to walk my sweet Eleanor down the aisle on her wedding day. More immediately, would I still be able to be the dad to her that I wanted to be?

I realized that as my Parkinson's progressed, I'd have more facial masking, where I would no longer be able to smile at my wife and daughter. When that happened, I'd need to say repeatedly, "No, I'm not mad. I just can't move my face to show you that I'm happy."

Then I thought about the late stages of the disease. I pictured myself leaning to one side in a wheelchair, not being able to walk. I thought of how claustrophobic it would feel when my brain was alert, but I would be trapped in my body. I envisioned my tremors making it impossible to hold a drink or use utensils to feed myself. *What will it be like, requiring help every time I have to use the bathroom? Will I become such a drag that no family member wants to be around? I will become a burden to every person in my family, and they don't deserve this. Am I going to want to live like this, or will it become unbearable?*

And then I looked down at my hand where I saw the contact case full of pills through my teary eyes. I was still at work, facing the early days of my Parkinson's diagnosis. But each time I reached for my medicine, my mind would race to the finish line—even though the starter pistol has just signaled the beginning of my Parkinson's race.

That was my depression, some days worse than others. I stayed stuck in this stage for a long time, unable to make big steps into acceptance.

"You have Parkinson's."

Your mind wants to always imagine the worst, even though the worst rarely happens. While any of these terrible things are possible, they are not guaranteed. When I thought about my deepest fears playing out in my future, my dark thoughts got worse. And my depression worsened as I learned more about Parkinson's treatment options like deep brain stimulation surgery. Will I have to have this surgery? If so, when will I need to have it done? There was no shortage of questions that were popping into my brain.

I knew about this procedure, but while attending the World Parkinson's Conference later, I'd hear about it in much more detail. It sounded so gruesome and scary, I had to leave the room as I got totally overwhelmed and went to tears. *How can it possibly be that I'm in this terrible situation?*

That phrase *knowledge is power* is true in many ways. But when I was stuck in depression, knowledge was fear. Every new piece of information I learned terrified me or made me feel more heartbroken. For example, there is no medical cure or slowing of the disease—just symptom control. Another fun fact —by the time you show symptoms enough to get diagnosed, over 50 percent of your dopamine-producing cells have already been lost. Reading the checklist of potential symptoms is like the best of the best—loss of voice, choking, psychosis, hallucinations, persistent constipation, loss of smell, etc. It also did not help that every five seconds they were running a Parkinson drug commercial that had a guy seeing things and hearing voices that were not there. It was also troubling to think I might have caused this with my actions—being around pesticides, growing up with well water, and various other things that were presented as possible causes during the conference.

I knew that I couldn't keep returning to this deep pit in my mind. I'd have good days and bad days. On my best days, I'd take my medicine and not spend much time dwelling on my disease. On my worst days, I'd wake up immediately remembering my prognosis, realizing that the bad dream was actually true and staying stuck in my head for hours.

I had to move beyond my depression, but I didn't yet know how. I needed some hope, some encouragement to replace the dark thoughts.

That's when I started working my mind back to the old positive Blake I'd been before any of this started. I stopped trying to fight the disease and decided to accept it.

"TIME

TO

TAKE

THE

PILLS..."

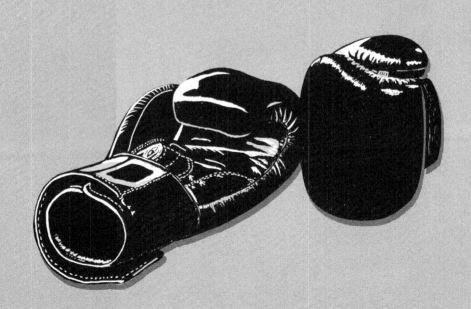

CHAPTER 5

EDUCATING MYSELF ABOUT THE DISEASE

By not telling people I had Parkinson's, I was able to outwardly live my life as if it were normal. But not really. When I was alone or with my family—and whenever I felt symptoms of the disease—my mind kept circling around it like a broken record.

I didn't lash out at other people, but my frustration showed up inside of me as I questioned if I'd done this to myself. And I spent hours researching everything I could learn about the disease.

Many people try to bargain when they're in grief. We've all seen movies where a character prays something like, "God, if you get me out of this, I'll go to church every Sunday and be nicer." I didn't pray that way. Instead, I said, "God, whatever happens, please let it be positive and help me get through this."

My dad once told me something I'll always remember: "Blake, play the cards you're dealt." Rather than bargain my way out of it, I did the best I could to play those cards.

The diagnosis handed me some bad cards, and my depression had added a couple more bad cards on the flop. In general, I found the best way to deal with it all was to keep myself busy. I needed time to process everything, and I found it easier to come to terms with my diagnosis in smaller steps, instead of trying to jump over it all at once.

In the next couple of months, I took three steps towards acceptance. I didn't know anything about the five stages of grief at the time, but I knew I didn't want to stay depressed or get stuck. So I made some changes, slowly at first. As I said, I started taking my medicine instead of letting it sit in my drawer. As I mentioned earlier, while the first neurologist had written me a prescription, I had never taken it. Then when the specialist, Dr. Morris, gave me the Parkinson's diagnosis and a different medication, I didn't take it right away either. I let the filled prescription sit there for a month before I finally tried it.

I finally took my first half-dose in February, following the doctor's recommendation of a half-pill to build up to three pills per day. Immediately, with just half of one pill, I felt a switch flip in my brain. I felt unreal, like a million bucks, just an hour or two after taking it. *WOW!* I was surprised by how good I felt.

The second thing I did was learn everything I could about my disease. Early on in my research, as I mentioned, I found all the possible ways that I might have brought this disease on myself. I realized that reading things like that did nothing to make me feel better, so this time, I started looking for where I could get a crash-course in Parkinson's, so I could know the best way to take care of myself and manage my symptoms.

I learned several things in the process. Since Parkinson's typically affects older people, young onset Parkinson's made me an outlier. Now, I love older people. But as I said in my introduction, many of the support groups and research articles were geared towards helping a more elderly population with the disease. I was still young and active, even with the disease. Many of the people I'd met with Parkinson's so far were of an age where they weren't still able to enjoy the physical lifestyle I had.

That's when I got Michael J. Fox's book, *Lucky Man*. I listened to him reading it instead of reading it myself. If you haven't already read or listened to this book, I strongly recommend it. Having been diagnosed with young onset Parkinson's at twenty-nine, Fox's story was relatable to me. Hearing him read his own story made Parkinson's more real, yet easier to accept. As someone who has watched *Family Ties* and the *Back to the Future* movies, Michael J. Fox seemed familiar, and learning that we shared young onset Parkinson's in common, he seemed almost like a friend.

Fox shared "what it's like to be a thirty-year-old man who is told he has an eighty-year-old's disease." Of course I wasn't thirty when I developed Parkinson's, but I felt his situation still paralleled my own. While that phrase might sound depressing, I knew that I'd learn a lot from him.

And then he said something in *Lucky Man* that I have held onto since: "Life is great. Sometimes, though, you just have to put up with a little more crap." Absolutely true. I knew I had a great life. If I let Parkinson's define me, the disease would win, and I would lose.

Soon after, I decided to find every way possible to help me put up with a little more crap instead of giving up.

After I'd finished listening to his book, I went to the internet to learn more. My doctor warned me about blindly searching the internet, but she said I could find the best information on Parkinsons.org and from the Michael J. Fox Foundation. My wife, Jennifer, started ordering books for me to read. She would read them as well. Through this reading she found a well-credentialed doctor she thought could help my situation and perhaps provide us with a second opinion.

Spotted in a doctor's office several years later.
It is hilarious.

Jennifer made an appointment for me with Dr. Rios at his clinic in December—ten months away. Neither of us could find a downside to making that appointment. In the meantime, I kept educating myself.

That's when I stumbled across the World Parkinson's Congress, a meeting that takes place every three years. Sometimes timing is everything. Had I been diagnosed a year later, I would have missed it, and would have had to wait a few years for the next one. When I learned that this year's conference would be held in Portland, Oregon, in September, I registered for my wife and I to attend. Then I saw that the Michael J. Fox Foundation held its own conference in New York City in October. *Why not?* I figured as I signed up for that conference, too. *When I take steps in the right direction, I feel better almost immediately.* Even though these events were still months away, they gave me something to look forward to.

In June, I took the third step towards accepting my disease when I watched a local news report about a military veteran, Zach, who organized and taught a Rock Steady Boxing class—a program for people with Parkinson's. I knew I had to get my stuff together. For years, I'd ridden my stationary bike for thirty minutes a few times per week, but I knew that wasn't enough to fight back against my progressive illness. I was intrigued, so I gave him a call. His training focused mainly on group boxing classes, but I wasn't interested in group classes. I figured there would be no harm in seeing if I could arrange some one-on-one physical training.

"Hi," I said over the phone. "I'm Blake. I just saw you on the news, and I'd be interested in having you as a personal trainer."

"Well, Blake," he said, his voice setting up to let me down gently, "I'm only working with people with Parkinson's right now."

"Well, I have Parkinson's," I said, almost excited that I qualified.

"Really?" he said, not questioning my honesty but out of sympathy. "My dad had Parkinson's, too. That's how I got into this. But you sound pretty young."

"I am," I told him. "I'm forty-seven."

"Maybe I can do something for you," Zach told me, mentioning that we could meet in his garage.

At this point, I was looking for three things. First, I wanted to avoid broadly "outing" myself with Parkinson's, so not attending group classes was key. Second, I knew I needed to get in some exercise, and since Zach had experience with helping his own dad, I figured he would know what kind of workouts to include. Finally, I hoped that I might meet some people in the Knoxville area in my own age group with Parkinson's.

While I didn't end up meeting anyone my age through Zach, I grew to "love" my workouts with him. That is, love them as much as anybody can love working out, because I found them so helpful. I still work out with him five years later. I never thought I would enjoy boxing as much as I do.

Fighting back

One thing I quickly learned was that most organizations that support people with Parkinson's work with a much older demographic. I had yet to find a local group that focused on young onset Parkinson's, or even one within driving distance. I hoped I would make some connections with people my age at the World Parkinson's conference.

In September, while my wife and I were at home, we heard ambulances coming into our neighborhood. We heard that a tree had fallen and killed someone. Then we learned that it was someone we knew—Ruthie, the wife of Bart, the man we'd purchased our home from years prior. Bart was on a mission trip at the time and rushed home. At Ruthie's funeral, Bart got up and spoke.

"Not many of you know this," he said, "but about six months ago, Ruthie was diagnosed with Parkinson's disease."

I was floored. Ruthie was close to my age, and like me, she had decided to fight it silently, not telling anybody about her diagnosis.

Later that month, I finally attended the World Parkinson's Congress, and I can't say enough good things about the experience. I found it funny when I saw on the schedule that sessions started at seven in the morning! I mean, most of us attending were already moving a little more slowly than people without Parkinson's. To even get downstairs in time to sign up for the sessions (which filled up fast), we had to wake up extremely early and rush to get ready. Even people without Parkinson's would find it difficult to beat the rush and get signed up early for something like this!

At one of the tables, I picked up a card from a sponsor that read, "I'm not drunk, I have Parkinson's disease." I smiled when I thought of giving one of these as a joke to Bryce.

Another interesting thing that happened is that I met Dr. Rios who spoke at the conference. After his session, I found him in the exhibit hall.

"Hi Doctor Rios," I said as I introduced myself and my wife to him. "I have an appointment to come see you at your clinic in December. I am really looking forward to it."

"Great," he replied. "Well, I look forward to seeing you then! We have quite a state-of-the-art facility there."

I was so happy to interact with him, because I knew he met hundreds of people at these events. But I hoped that a personal introduction would show him that I took my disease seriously and was hungry to treat it effectively. I wanted him to remember me.

But the highlight of the conference for me was a roundtable I attended for those with young onset Parkinson's. Each group had a credentialed facilitator or two from the congress as well as participants who were passionate about the topic. I joined a small group of ten or so people "like me"—which was incredibly gratifying. These conferences bring together thousands of people from all around the world, along with caregivers, rehabilitation specialists, nurses, physicians, researchers, scientists, pharmaceutical industry members, and exhibitors. But I believe the people at my table that morning were chosen just for me.

Prior to attending the conference, I had filled out a questionnaire that partnered me up with another attendee to talk with beforehand so that we would know someone when we got there. My partner was named Laura, and she was from Washington. We spoke on the phone, and it was interesting, hearing about her situation and how her Parkinson's developed. Then our partners chatted a little too, since they also had something in common—being married to someone with the disease.

I also met a few others who I truly enjoyed. John, a venture capitalist from Alaska, was my age and had had the same arm issues as me. We met for cocktails after the meetings were over. Jennifer and I also had dinner a couple of times with Laura and her husband. I also met Cathy from Ireland, a lady named Trudi, and a guy named Rex who worked for the owners of an NFL football team.

Finally, there was a twelve-year-old girl at our table. Twelve! And she was in bad shape, having difficulty moving even on medication. Compared to her, I was a picture of health. My heart went out to her.

Throughout the day, people talked about their worries and concerns. One guy was worried about how he would earn a living. Another was worried that he might get fired before he reached his retirement status if he told anyone about his diagnosis. Another attendee was worried about finances. I was very thankful that I didn't have these additional stressors to contend with, but I really sympathized with those who did.

It's hard to explain why this experience meant so much to me. But I loved connecting with people my own age and younger, and with familiar issues. I also loved sharing resources.

Someone brought up the topic of Michael J. Fox's book *Lucky Man,* and several people made a note to read it. Cathy created a Facebook group for all of us, so we could keep in touch. John and I still speak every six months or so.

I also met a woman named Ruth, who was probably in her late sixties. Trained in nursing, she worked as the business development person for a Parkinson's center. She knew her stuff, and she really knew how to relate to us. She's still probably the best person I've ever talked with about the disease.

In the exhibit hall, I found an "ask the doctor about research" panel with three experts welcoming questions. I sat in on the discussion and found myself wondering if I wanted to get involved with clinical trials. Early on, I had signed up for the Michael J Fox Foundations' Fox Trial Finder, since they aggregated research opportunities across the world. When you join, they can match you up with opportunities.

Attending the educational seminar, I met an expert doctor from Duke University Medical Center, who stole the show. No matter what question was asked, he would have the most comprehensive answer, along with a simple way of explaining complicated medical subjects. Had I not already connected with Dr. Rios, I would have jumped at the chance to use this doctor at Duke.

The conference gave me hope from many angles, like a man I met from the Davis Phinney Foundation. John was in his sixties and dealing with his own Parkinson's diagnosis. Still, he had nothing but optimism. He could see that I was a bit overwhelmed, so he took Jennifer and me under his wing, inviting us out to a group dinner. There, he told us about his upcoming brain surgery, planned a few months in the future, with Dr. Rios's colleague as the surgeon. John would be the first patient in the United States to be implanted with a new model of brain stimulation device. I later talked to him after his brain surgery, and he told me it was the best thing he ever did.

"YOU'LL FALL AND GET HURT..."

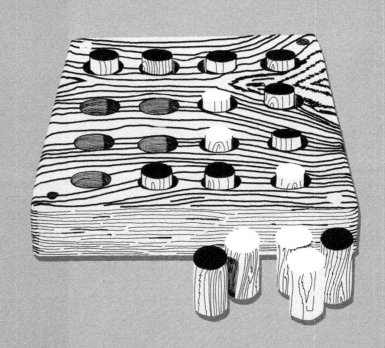

CHAPTER 6

LEARNING FROM THE EXPERTS

WE FLEW HOME FROM OREGON, BEFORE PACKING another bag and heading out again to New York City for the Michael J. Fox Foundation conference. It didn't take me long to realize that this was a different sort of conference. When I booked it, I thought it would be another education session or retail session for Parkinson's patients. It wasn't. It was more of a private conference for doctors.

This conference was held at Convene, a company that operates meeting spaces in high-rise buildings across the city. It was a really well-done event in a nice facility, with plenty of canned and bottled beverages and numerous snacks. I found 555 Park Avenue with no problem, but I didn't see any signs telling me where to go. Finally, I saw a poster with the word "Convene," and an arrow on it. I asked the guard who told me we were in the right place. After taking our names, he told us the floor number and pointed to the elevator.

When the elevator delivered us and the doors opened, I saw a very intimate meeting place. Once we had checked in, we went to a small area where they had a continental breakfast, and people were socializing until the meeting started.

Jennifer and I sat at a table, and shortly afterwards, another person sat down to join us. To my surprise, it was Dr. Rios. What a coincidence!

"Hi, Doctor Rios," I said. "I'm not sure if you remember me, but I met you last week in Portland, Oregon, and I'm coming to see you in December. I also met a couple of your nurses while I was there."

"Oh, sure," he said as he shook my hand.

"Anyway, I just wanted to say hello again," I told him as I went to grab a Diet Coke from the endless supply they had available.

As more people came to our table, the doctor-talk began. As I listened to the medical terminology and banter, I realized this conference was not what I had envisioned it to be. When I'd told my new friends the previous week that I'd be attending this event, none of them had even heard of it. *Perhaps this is why*, I thought.

It was getting close to starting time. I found a seat in the meeting room and started to review the binder of information I'd been given when I checked in. It included a directory of people who were attending the conference. Around me, I heard doctors, most of whom seemed to know each other, talking shop.

"Well, this particular patient had blah blah blah" and "my research project blah blah blah" is all I could hear, but I was intrigued as well as amused to listen in.

How do I get myself in these situations? I thought with a smile on my face. Yeah, this is a very different kind of conference...

Soon, I met a pharmaceutical representative who filled me in a bit.

"Yeah, this conference is mainly for doctors and people related to the Parkinson's field, but I think you'll learn some interesting things," he said.

Once again, Dr. Rios spoke, which I found fascinating. He showed a video of patients who had been recorded at his clinic —the same place I'd be visiting in December. The patients shared on camera which trials and studies they were participating in, and how differently they responded to various interventions.

Another doctor was giving an update on the PPMI (Parkinson's Progression Markers Initiative) study. The doctors were commenting that even though they had a lot of people giving their DNA, they'd had a hard time finding volunteers who would go the distance and not drop out of the study later. This is because more advanced testing involved spinal punctures. *Not a big surprise why people weren't racing to continue participating in that study*, I thought.

We stayed most of the day, and as my new friend in pharmaceutical sales promised, I did learn some interesting things. I met a naturopath out of Seattle, as well as another researcher in the process of redesigning a brain stimulator. I also got the attendee list that included everyone's contact information. I had numbers to call if I ever needed anything.

A little bedtime reading

I'm not sure I would attend again, but I'm glad I went. You never know when you might make a new connection that could change your life for the better.

I'd heard about this 23andMe study for Parkinson's disease. The company at the time gave Parkinson's patients a free test, so they could offer your data to drug companies. Typically I'm Mr. Privacy, but this seemed like a win-win situation.

I would win by getting the test done and contributing to research; 23andMe likely would make a good buck selling the data to researchers; and the pharmaceutical companies could get data to create more effective and first-to-market treatment options.

23andMe sent me a raw dump of my genetic data. Which, of course, made no sense to me.

I was also able to see my ethnic makeup. The results showed that I had some Ashkenazi Jewish ancestry—22.4 percent to be exact. (My DNA report also said, by the way, that I have more Neanderthal DNA than 38 percent of their other customers. Go figure. I wasn't sure what I should do with that information...)

Jennifer and I had the same doctor. When Jennifer went to one of her own appointments, the doctor asked her about my ethnicity.

"Unfortunately," our doctor told Jennifer, "research shows that people with Ashkenazi Jewish ancestry are more susceptible to many different diseases." As it turned out, my ancestry put me more at risk for a mutated GBA gene. That genetic mutation increases the odds for Parkinson's disease.

Not much I can change about that; it is what it is, I thought when my wife told me.

Finally, in December, I packed my bags and headed for my long-awaited appointment with Dr. Rios. My wife and I flew in a day early so we would be rested for the following day.

The Movement Clinic was known as the most advanced center in the world for treating Parkinson's. Not only was Dr. Rios a sought-after expert on Parkinson's, but also many of his colleagues were experts in different facets of the disease as well. After waiting for ten months to get there, I had secretly hoped this visit would shed light on a "magic bullet"—some new treatment I had not heard of—that would change the standard prognosis of my Parkinson's.

I'd been instructed not to take any of my medication on the day of the appointment. Dr. Rios's office wanted to evaluate me cold, in other words, with nothing in my system. Essentially, they wanted to see me at my worst, unmedicated state.

When we arrived, the staff took us to a conference room to sign several papers, one of which was to grant them permission to make video recordings of our sessions for future training purposes. *Damned if you do, damned if you don't,* I figured. *If I refuse, they might view me as uncooperative. If I comply, who knows how it will be used?* I figured I'd consent in the hopes that whatever they found might be helpful to those coming after me on this journey.

Next, they took me to an occupational therapist, who ran me through multiple exercises. One of the most revealing was a "game" where they timed me putting pegs into different holes with each hand separately. Think of it like a version of the tabletop peg game at your local Cracker Barrel restaurant. But this one wasn't about solving a puzzle. Instead, the researchers were testing my manual dexterity. I managed forty-five pegs with my left hand but only thirty-two with my right hand. I could hardly believe how much less coordination I had on my right side.

"I'm going to buy one of these so I can practice at home," I joked with the physical therapist.

"Oh, no! That's cheating," she joked back. "But seriously, don't do that. It'll screw up our test data if you practice. We just do this to get an accurate baseline."

I joked, but I was still shocked at how impaired I had become. I had expected my two hands to show closer results.

"Do you sit down when you put your clothes on?" she asked.

"No," I told her. "I stand up."

"That's terrible," she answered with a grimace. "You're going to fall and get hurt."

"Maybe," I said, "but I see it as kind of a balancing act. Doing things like that makes my balance sharper. I would rather stand up and risk falling than sit and lose whatever skills I have."

"I don't advise you doing that," she continued.

"Noted," I said with a smile, letting her know that I'd keep doing what I was doing.

Then they introduced me to a man who put me through a battery of written questions to better understand my mental state. I filled out the questionnaire and handed it back to him. While scanning my responses, he asked me a few questions.

"Let me just look at one thing," he said, trying to find a certain question.

"Are you looking for the one that asks if I'm thinking of harming myself?" I joked.

"Yes, and you got that answer right!" he replied.

Part of me wondered why they bothered asking, figuring it must have something to do with liability. Either way, I wasn't thinking of hurting myself. *But if I were*, I thought, *would I check YES on that box? I mean, who would do that?*

Before I met with Dr. Rios, they brought in one of his proteges.

After examining me for a bit, his protege asked me if I had any questions. I always did in these settings, and this time was no different.

"Yes," I answered, before asking my signature question I ask of all doctors: "If I were your son or daughter, what would you advise me to do?"

I didn't want to be patient #8853-0921. I wanted the doctors to guide me with the same care as if I were a loved one.

In this specific moment, I wanted to know, "Should I be taking carbidopa/ levodopa, or should I be taking a dopamine agonist?" I asked.

From my reading and the conferences I'd attended, I knew there was a big debate over which class of Parkinson's medication I should take given my age. One school of thought is that I should be on carbidopa/levodopa, a class of drugs that increases dopamine levels. That's what I currently was taking. The potential problem I found is that it can cause dyskinesias over time, giving me muscle spasms and jerky motions. I hated the thought of that. The other class of drugs were dopamine agonists, chemicals that activate dopamine receptors in the brain.

Parkinson's disease messes with dopamine levels in the brain. By the time most people with the disease get diagnosed, the cells that produce, absorb, and use dopamine have already begun to die. Medical treatments are designed to increase the level of dopamine that your body needs to control movements. Carbidopa/levodopa converts levodopa into dopamine, and dopamine agonists stop your brain from breaking down dopamine, so it uses dopamine at a more normal level. The two classes of drugs achieve the same thing but work by different mechanisms, and they have different side-effects.

"My second question," I followed up, "is can you help me decode the DNA from 23andMe?"

"If you send it to me," Dr. Rios's protege offered, "I will decode it for you."

Unfortunately, that never happened, but he did give me his opinion about what medication he thought I should be taking.

"I don't think you should be on carbidopa/levodopa," he said flatly. "I'd put you on a dopamine agonist."

"Which one?"

"Probably Mirapex," the doctor replied.

"Really? Why is that?" I pushed.

"Well, given your age," he started, before reciting all the reasons I already knew.

"That really surprises me, but it makes sense," I told him when he finished. "But I have to say, I'm worried about gambling all my money away or something worse."

Yeah, a possible side-effect of taking a dopamine agonist is that you lose the filter or governor that keeps your actions in check. I didn't like the thought of losing my governor. I'm really good at keeping my cool and staying patient in most situations. But there is a very thin line, and my governor, keeps me in check—as opposed to screaming obscenities at someone or blurting out things that I would later regret.

"Yes," the doctor conceded, "loss of impulse control is a possibility."

Before we could finish our conversation, Dr. Rios came in, along with four other students. Having read my records and recent test results, he wasted no time before examining me quickly and giving me an opinion on my medication.

"You are woefully undermedicated," he pronounced without fanfare. "You are taking three pills a day. You need to be taking six."

"Really? That seems like a lot of pills," I questioned. "I feel great with just the three."

"I've got patients taking twenty a day," he responded.

"I thought there was an upper limit," I said, wanting to know more.

"Well, there's no established limit. It's based on what your body can handle," he answered.

Then he gave me a more comprehensive answer about why he thought I should be increasing my dose of carbidopa/levodopa. While Dr. Rios didn't say these exact words, he essentially told me, *Look, this medication will help you feel the best you're ever going to feel. It only gets worse from here. Take advantage of it while you can.* He said the biggest mistake he saw in people with Parkinson's make was not taking enough medication early on.

I knew I'd eventually reach a point where the carbidopa/levodopa wouldn't last as long as it had in the past. Instead of each pill giving me six hours of relief, I would get five, then four, etc. And at some point, no additional medication would change that. Maybe a surgery or a supplement with another drug could help, but it would become a delicate balance of tweaking drug combinations. And in the end, I would never feel better than the 100 percent I felt when taking the medication.

His recommendation came down to this: *take as many pills as needed to feel as close to 100 percent for as long as possible.*

"I understand, but I don't want to develop medication-induced dyskinesia. Won't more medication make that more likely or make it happen sooner?" I wanted to know. Dyskinesia is uncontrolled, involuntary movement that can happen with long-term levodopa use as Parkinson's progresses.

I figured if I could get by on taking three pills a day for the next four years, wouldn't that potentially delay dyskinesias longer than if I were to take six pills a day now?

While his protege stood next to him, Dr. Rios said emphatically, "You need to be taking six pills a day."

"Well," I responded, "I'm confused. The doctor next to you just told me I shouldn't even be on carbidopa/levodopa. He thinks I should be on a dopamine agonist like Mirapex."

There I was with a world-class neurologist and a doctor working with him in his clinic, and they had conflicting thoughts on what I needed. I would take Dr. Rios's advice, given his expertise, but obviously I hoped the two of them would have given me the same answer.

"Well," Dr. Rios said quickly, "I disagree. I think you need to take carbidopa/levodopa, not Mirapex."

This was my first experience with something that I'd later learn while trying to find the optimal treatment. Getting consensus about Parkinson's treatment from doctors—even experts in the field—is sometimes difficult. The disease is complicated, and so are the pros and cons of the medication options. What works for some patients doesn't work for others, and often, the best way to know what works comes down to trial and error.

Back at the World Parkinson's Congress, I had talked with John and Laura, who I had met in the small group discussion of other young onset Parkinson's sufferers. Both were on Mirapex and seemed surprised that I'd been given carbidopa/levodopa.

"Wow!" I remember John saying when he first learned that I was on carbidopa/levodopa. "That's wild at your age."

But Laura wasn't exactly a positive advertisement for Mirapex. One side-effect of the medication was causing her to see things flying across her field of vision that were not real, like little gnats buzzing around. I remember thinking, *Laura gets gnats. I'm not sure I could handle seeing gnats that weren't there.*

After waiting so long for my appointment with Dr. Rios, I ended up disappointed. I am not being critical of him or his institute but I had mistakenly built up such high expectations for this appointment that I had also set myself up to feel disheartened. I would not get that 100 percent "here is what you should do" treatment recommendation I had hoped for.

I guess I'm back to the drawing board, I told myself as I began a new search for the right doctor.

Once home, I became a bit obsessed about getting my DNA data analyzed but I could not get anyone to read the raw dump file from 23andMe. At the time, direct-to-consumer genome companies like them were not permitted to interpret the results. But I really wanted to know which gene mutation I had.

In November, I ended up enrolling in the PPMI study and sending them my DNA sample. I signed up for a DNA test, although not the one with the spinal punctures. I didn't know what would come of it, but I was delighted several months later when I got a letter saying that they had analyzed my sample and determined that I did have a mutation in the GBA gene.

Their analysis of my DNA led me to the Silverstein Foundation, an organization that focuses on research regarding mutations of the GBA gene. Although the research regarding different genes and their mutations is in its infancy, one day they hopefully will help lead to treatments.

"You've Got To Pick One..."

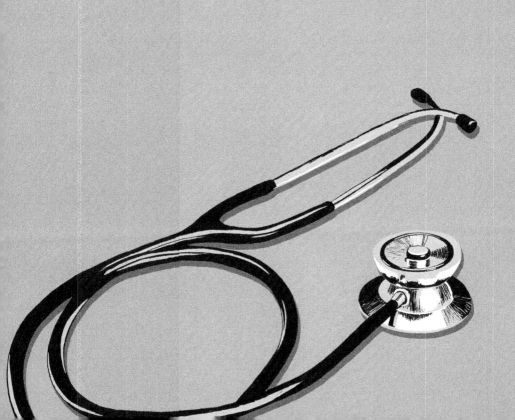

Chapter 7

Doctor Shopping

I returned home after my appointment, depressed that Dr. Rios offered no magic bullet. Many doctors could diagnose and treat Parkinson's. A few, like Dr. Rios, were deep specialists in the field.

But I wanted more than that. I wanted Dr. Right, the provider that felt like a perfect "fit" for me.

After a couple of months, I decided to research more about the doctor from Duke—the doctor I'd first heard speak at the World Parkinson's Congress. He had also run the Muhammad Ali Parkinson's Center in Arizona. I made an appointment to see him in May of 2017, and Jennifer and I were soon traveling to Raleigh, North Carolina to meet him.

When my appointment began, I had high hopes. My first meeting was with a graduate student who asked me great questions. She felt like a respected colleague of the doctor I'd be meeting. I had a great feeling about this place, largely because of my interaction with her.

Heck, even if I don't get much face time with the doctor, this student is fantastic. I can see myself working with her, I thought. And that's when she told me she was returning home to Iceland after she had completed her studies.

"Okay, that's a little further than I wanted to travel, but I think you'd be worth the trip!" I joked with her to hide my disappointment.

When the doctor came in, I loved him immediately. He was direct and honest about what my future could hold, even though it wasn't all rosy. However, I didn't shoot the messenger. I found him knowledgeable, and I also could see myself working with him. Jennifer got the same vibe, and that was enough confirmation for me to move forward.

As the appointment was wrapping up, I felt like I needed to say something.

"You know, I'm forty-seven, and I've seen multiple doctors already since my diagnosis. I just want to make sure that you're going to be here for ten or so years and are not planning on retiring soon or anything. Are you?"

He returned a puzzled look. "No, why do you ask?"

"Well, if I'm considering changing my doctor to you, I want to make sure that you'll be around."

"Ah," he answered. "That makes sense."

He assured me that he had every intention of staying with Duke.

Unfortunately, though, when I went to transfer my records over to Duke only a month or two later, I learned that he was no longer practicing medicine. Instead, he had taken up a position to head up a medical school.

Once again, my high expectations led me to disappointment.

Then I figured that even if he couldn't be my doctor, he might be able to lead me to the best ones still practicing.

"Okay, I know you're no longer practicing, but who would you recommend to a member of your own family?" I emailed him.

"I really hate giving out recommendations, since I know so many great doctors," he replied.

"Look," I said, playing my trump card, "I'm not trying to be a pain, but when I was there, you told me that you'd be sticking around for the long haul. Since you're not, I'd appreciate it if you could recommend someone else. You seem very smart and knowledgeable. I want someone like you. Who would you see if you were me?"

"I don't mind giving you a few names," he stated. "Just please don't broadcast the names I don't give you, okay?"

Then he told me three names—doctors in Georgia, Minnesota, and Arizona. I quickly ruled out Arizona, since the other two doctors were closer.

"Thank you," I said sincerely.

I emailed the two remaining doctors. The doctor in Minnesota responded first.

"I'm happy to see you here in Minnesota," he told me, "but you have some great doctors much closer to you. Like Vanderbilt."

"I'm with Vanderbilt currently, but I'm looking for a change," I told him.

Dr. Morris at Vanderbilt for sure knew her stuff, and I had no doubts that she was a great doctor. But do you know that *Seinfeld* line from George, "It's not you, it's me"? That's how I felt about Dr. Morris and Vanderbilt. My desire to find a new doctor really didn't have anything to do with Dr. Morris; it had to do with my own post-traumatic stress from that appointment when I was first diagnosed with Parkinson's. I didn't want to go back to Vanderbilt because of the memories associated with that heartbreaking day.

"So if I leave Vanderbilt and want to stay closer to home than, say, Minnesota, where would you send a family member with Parkinson's in my area?"

"Dr. Turner at Emory University in Atlanta is fantastic," he said without hesitation.

"It's great to hear that," I told him. "Another neurologist gave me your name, as well as Dr. Turner's. So for you to mention Dr. Turner, too, makes me feel a lot more comfortable."

"He's really good," the doctor assured me. "And you're only about three hours away from him."

I wrote to Dr. Turner's direct email address, outlining my situation, and indicated I wanted to schedule an appointment with him. To my surprise, he replied in about 15 minutes.

I wanted the best care I could find. That meant I wanted both a solid neurologist with expertise in Parkinson's and someone I could establish a good rapport with. Unfortunately, it's easier to find a doctor with one of those traits than both. And researching to find the best takes time.

Since Jennifer made up my entire inner circle, I bounced ideas off her. Finally, she offered some great advice.

"You've got to pick one, Blake." As usual, she was right. I had three or four potential leads on the "right" doctor already, but I was wasting time. I didn't know if I had found my idea of "perfect," but after my appointment with Dr. Turner, he seemed to be a great fit. Since he was the director of the Emory Parkinson's Disease Center and Movement Disorder Program, he had to know his stuff. And he had now come double recommended by other prominent doctors.

"You're right," I told Jennifer a short time later. "I'm going with Dr. Turner and Emory, and believe I will be in good hands."

As an aside, I talked again to John from Alaska, the friend I'd made at the World Parkinson's Congress. After we caught up, he told me something interesting.

"I switched from Mirapex to carbidopa/levodopa," he said.

"What?" I asked. "When we talked last time, you were really puzzled that I was taking it."

"Well," John answered, "Mirapex wasn't working as well, so we decided to tweak it. That led me to carbidopa/levodopa. And I have to say, I see now why you like it."

Once I heard that, I felt better about my journey. For all the traits I liked and disliked about the many specialists I'd encountered, it seemed I had been on the right treatment course all along.

I also knew that the time had now come for me to start telling more people about my diagnosis.

CHAPTER 8

OPENING UP

EVEN THOUGH I WASN'T WILLING TO OPEN MYSELF UP TO everyone about my Parkinson's early on, I had told Bryce the day I received my diagnosis. At that point, I had not yet decided whether to share or not share more widely about having Parkinson's. Bryce and I had seen each other the night before that call, so he knew why I was going to Nashville. When he had called me to find out how my first visit with the neurologist had gone, I didn't filter my answer. But shortly after that call with Bryce, Jennifer and I had decided that we would keep the information between us.

But before long, I needed to tell a few family members. It was hard at first to even utter the word *Parkinson's*. When I thought about opening up about it, I would tear up a bit, and my voice couldn't even say the word—like I lost all power trying to make sound come out.

I used the word *heartbroken* to describe how my Parkinson's diagnosis had made me feel. For whatever reason, whenever I started going down the path of trying to tell someone, my heartbreak grew even stronger. Even now, years later, it chokes me up. But I will say it's gotten easier to talk about.

I needed to tell my family, but I also needed to tell them in the right order and at the right time, because the last thing I wanted was for my six-year old daughter, Eleanor, to find out about my Parkinson's from anyone other than me. I could not imagine my daughter hearing such news secondhand.

It was around six months after my initial diagnosis that I decided that the first person in my family that I would tell would be my sister, Jessica, who lived only a few miles away. While I was ten years older, we'd always been and continue to be very close.

Around the same time, Jennifer and I were facing some crucial decisions to do with a major remodeling project that we were having done on our home. Our house was first built in 1896. That meant we pretty much needed to rebuild it to make it fit for modern living. The project was already well underway when I got my diagnosis. That got us thinking, *since we're going to be here a while, should we put up grab bars up in the shower? Should we put in a handicapped toilet?* Those changes were fairly minor but, there were potentially bigger changes to consider, too. *Should we put in an elevator in case I get to the point where I have problems getting up and down the stairs?* If so, that would need to be engineered and the plans would have to be altered now, because we were already at a point in the construction and design phase where this kind of request would already be pushing it.

The construction foreman proposed putting in some steps from the garage to the main house.

"Listen," I told him, "I'm going to need you to flatten that out and not put those steps in."

He didn't understand why, but he found a way to do what I'd asked for. But as Jennifer and I continued talking about the future, we knew we needed to make bigger decisions about the rest of the construction, and I decided to pull the foreman aside for a talk.

"I need to share something with you, but I need you to not say anything to anyone else, okay?" I started. And then I told him about my diagnosis.

We opted to add the elevator. As far as adding grab bars around the toilet and showers, we decided at this stage to add reinforced wood behind the walls to support those, should they be needed in the future. As for the toilet, we passed on installing a handicap-accessible one, wanting to keep the visual signs of my diagnosis away a little longer. Why prematurely remind myself with daily visuals?

In the midst of all this, I also called my sister.

"Hey, if you get some time today or this week, can you come over to my office?" I asked. My "office" was the home we'd bought next door to our own. I needed the extra office and workout space, and it doubled as a guesthouse when we had company or business associates.

When she stopped by, she had no idea what I was about to drop on her.

"What's up?" she asked.

In my office/guesthouse, we had two couches facing each other. We sat across the coffee table from one another, and I started.

"Hey, I just wanted to let you know that... you know... I have Parkinson's."

Stressful situations have a way of either making memories sharper or foggier. The words didn't come out easily, and I don't remember if she teared up or not. But she immediately tried to keep the conversation upbeat.

"Okay, okay, yeah, well, you know..." she fumbled to find the right words. "You know... we'll get through this, no problem."

Once I say those five little words, "I have young onset Parkinson's," and I get the acknowledgement that someone gets it, it always becomes easier for me to detach from my emotions and start talking intellectually about the disease. Once I know that the other person understands, I become an open book. After I have said the word *Parkinson's*, I even feel comfortable adding, "ask me any questions you want. Nothing is too personal. I'm happy to answer anything."

Jessica hugged me tight.

"I haven't told Mom and Dad yet," I told her before she left. "I will. I just don't know when. I need to tell Eleanor, too. But for now, I want everyone to treat me like they always have. I don't know how long I can keep my anonymity with my diagnosis."

I knew I couldn't hide the tremors forever. Some people might wonder why I didn't smile much. I didn't isolate myself from other people, but I didn't want to have to explain my condition to everyone I met either, especially since I had so much trouble initially getting the words out of my mouth whenever I told someone. *You can't unring a bell,* I thought. *I'll keep the group of those who know about my Parkinson's small for as long as I can.*

I told Jessica that she could tell her husband Matt, but I asked her not to tell their daughters yet since I didn't want the information to get back to Eleanor.

A few months later, I knew the time had finally come to tell my parents. After I dropped Eleanor off at school, I pulled into a parking lot and shut off the car. I took a deep breath, and then I called them at home.

"Hey, Dad," I said, trying to sound as casual as possible, "Could you maybe get Mom on the phone, too?"

Once they both picked up, I started.

"So, you know I've had these tremors," I said. I swallowed hard before continuing, not wanting any *woe is me* to come across in my voice. "I have Parkinson's."

"Oh no, I hate that," my dad said immediately.

Mom said something very similar.

"I'm sorry for not telling you sooner, but I needed to get my head around it all first, both emotionally and intellectually. Also, I wanted to keep it from Eleanor for as long as possible. I'll tell her when I feel it is right."

That was a hard phone call. I could tell Dad was shaken by the news, and Mom was sad to hear her little boy had Parkinson's.

A few days later, I got together with them to answer any questions they might have and to give them more information, including a blow-by-blow account of my trips to Oregon and New York City.

A year had now passed since my diagnosis, and I still hadn't told my daughter. She was seven years old, and I didn't want to throw her world into chaos. She'd already started asking questions about death, like most seven-year-olds do. I remembered having the same thoughts when I was her age, like, *What would I do if my parents died?* But I didn't want to be the one to force her mind to think about death and disease. I wanted it to come up naturally in a conversation, so it wouldn't have to be such a "big deal."

One of the best things I learned from Michael J. Fox's book was how he normalized Parkinson's when he talked about it with his son. Fox referred to himself as "shaky daddy" when he struggled to control his hands. He'd make a game out of it with his son to see how long he could keep his hands steady. They would count together.

One day I found a natural opportunity to talk with Eleanor. As I drove and Eleanor was buckled in the booster chair in the back seat, my hand and arm had a twitch. She noticed it.

"Why did your hand shake, Daddy?" she asked.

"Well, it's because I have Parkinson's," I answered simply. "It's no big deal, but sometimes you're going to see me shake. You know what I mean?"

"I knew it!" she said as if she had just solved a mystery that she'd been keeping to herself.

But that's when I knew that she'd already seen enough signs of my disease to guess that something was not quite right. She was more perceptive at her age than I gave her credit for.

As of the writing of this book, Eleanor is now thirteen, and she understands way more stuff than I would have ever thought. She's always been a very smart girl. I have no doubt that she's been on the internet looking up Parkinson's in the years since I first told her about my disease.

I'm so glad that she and I can finally talk openly about it. I'm now an open book about my disease, willing to answer any question she might have. Of course, it's really hard and it doesn't help matters when she hears things about Parkinson's from television commercials. While the two of us were watching television one day, a commercial for the drug NUPLAZID came on. The voice said something like, "Seventy percent of patients with Parkinson's get visions, psychosis, and hallucinations." I was sure that certain people got psychosis, but probably for anything, not just Parkinson's.

Great, I thought. *Now I'm going to have to have a conversation about psychosis?*

I explained to her that the ad had some truth. Psychosis is way more common in someone diagnosed later in life than it is with someone who is diagnosed younger. Parkinson's appears to affect older people's brains differently than it does someone at my age.

More recently, Eleanor started asking me if I would die from Parkinson's.

"No, cutie," I assured her. "That's the good thing about Parkinson's. You die *with* it, but not *from* it," I told her, repeating a phrase I learned along my journey.

Once I let Eleanor know about my Parkinson's, I started telling a handful of my closest friends. I never found it *easy*, but it did become *easier*. And after I had told the people who were most important to me, I didn't care who knew.

That's when I intentionally told a family friend who then functioned like the "town crier" of old. I told her about my Parkinson's and asked her to keep it quiet. Within a month, just about everyone who knew me had heard the news.

Today, telling people about my diagnosis is more of an "elephant in the room" kind of situation. People see me and quickly know that something is"off." So in general, I try to get ahead of it instead of letting people speculate.

When my dad and I went to buy a property together, for example, we met with the sellers who happened to be an older couple. I kept my hands in my coat pockets to try to hide my trembling but I could tell the woman noticed. After many years in business, I can tell you that looking nervous or shady doesn't help in negotiations. (Heck, for all I knew, the poor woman might have thought I had a gun in my pocket!)

Instead of letting the proverbial elephant continue to take up space in our conversation, I weaved the information in naturally.

"We sold our last business in Kentucky," I told them. "My dad is in his late seventies, and I have Parkinson's, so we thought it made sense to sell it. We liked your property as an investment, because it's simpler to manage."

I've found that once I tell people I have Parkinson's—even strangers like the couple with whom my dad and I were negotiating—they often understand and say something supportive, like "oh, my grandfather had that" or "my neighbor has Parkinson's, too."

Who knows? Maybe they even feel a little sorry for me and give me a better price! I say that as a joke, but at some point, you must be willing to laugh about it.

THE BOOKSTAFFS:
ME, JENNIFER AND ELEANOR

ME, MY AWESOME SISTER
JESSICA AND MY DAD

ELEANOR AND I
AXE-THROWING WITH MY
MOM AND DAD – TWO OF
THE BEST PARENTS A GUY
COULD ASK FOR

HANGING OUT
WITH BEST FRIENDS,
BILL AND BRYCE

"IT

IS

WHAT

IT

IS..."

CHAPTER 9

ACCEPTING MY DISEASE

THE BIGGEST BREAKTHROUGH THAT ALLOWED ME TO MOVE forward happened when I had finally made peace with my diagnosis, recognizing *it is what it is*.

Six distinct actions helped me to accept my diagnosis:

- Looking forward to something positive
- Finding joy in work
- Taking my medication
- Learning more about Parkinson's
- Participating in research studies
- Changing my perspective

I want to explain how each of these played a role in helping me get "unstuck" after my diagnosis. My hope is that you will find some ideas that will work for you, too.

LOOK FORWARD TO SOMETHING POSITIVE

Here's the part of the story where I tell you more about that electric car I bought, as I promised I'd do.

Before I was diagnosed with Parkinson's, my dad and I were in Orlando and saw a Tesla dealer.

"Hey, Dad," the gadget-head in me said, "you want to go look at a Tesla?"

"Sure, let's do it," he said agreeably.

In the Orlando showroom

Looking turned into a test drive, and driving it blew me away.

"You ought to buy one of those for yourself," my dad said when he saw my excitement.

"Do you think it's worth it?" I asked, experiencing sticker shock.

"What does it matter? You've worked hard, you can afford it, and you should buy it," he said. This was very atypical talk for my dad. He's the kind of guy who would take a used turquoise colored truck that nobody would buy just because it was $500 off.

"Well, I want one. But if I get a Tesla, I'm going to look for a used one," I responded while talking myself into the idea.

I did as much research on the Tesla as possible before deciding on my next move. Long story short, I saved a good deal of money and won a bid on eBay for a one-year-old Tesla Model S. Before long, my dad and I went out to Newport Beach, California, to pick it up.

The Tesla I bought is fast, going from 0 to 60 in 3.2 seconds. (The previous owner had named it Millennium Falcon, which pretty much explains it!)

It can drive itself on the road, staying in the center of the lane and steering the wheel around curves. It knows the speed limit, even in work zones. And every three weeks or so, I get an update with new features. That means, unlike most cars, this one keeps getting better.

The other day, they added Spotify, so now I can tell it to play any song I can think of while driving. Another feature they added is called "dog mode," and it keeps the air conditioning or heat on when you're out of the car. It's even got arcade games that you can play on a big screen. And Elon Musk, besides being a PR genius, also has a weird sense of humor, so it's even got hidden jokes and undocumented features that people discover and talk about.

The updates are never-ending. The car even locks itself when you walk away from it.

Have you ever almost scraped a curb that was too high? The car is smart enough to remember that curb, and the car will raise up to miss the curb the next time you go to that location, before you even get there.

At this point, you might be wondering how a car helped me accept my diagnosis and learn how to move beyond it. Well, after I was diagnosed, I knew that the progressive nature of the disease would continue to depreciate my body. When you receive such news, you go into a sort of shock. At least for me with my always-thinking brain, I couldn't help thinking about it and obsessing about it, over and over and over.

I didn't consciously realize this, but what I needed initially was something for my mind to focus on and to keep it busy. The Tesla became the first thing that occupied and filled up mindshare. This is because I love technology and was fascinated by the car and the way the engineers kept coming up with new features to add. To me, it was revolutionary. I felt like I was driving the car of the future.

I had even looked forward to all the studying and research I did before I bought it. I loved driving it. And it came to represent something that engaged me and looked forward to. Elon Musk said, "I think a Tesla is the most fun thing you could possibly buy ever." And that pretty much summed it up for me.

I just can't believe I own this thing!

Am I saying it is time for you to rush out and buy a Tesla? No, but having *something* to look forward to certainly kept me going when times were rough.

My next fascination was Bitcoin and cryptocurrency, but that is another story. The point that I am trying to make is this: what is it that you love and look forward to doing? Maybe it's gardening or just being out in nature. Perhaps you love learning new things, spending time with family, writing, or traveling. Whatever it is that gives you the thrill of anticipation, this is *your Tesla*. Invest in it now, and enjoy it. Having something positive on the horizon that forces itself into your mindshare keeps your focus on what is great in your life.

FIND JOY IN WORK

I consider myself blessed to love my work. As a serial entrepreneur, I always have multiple projects going on and in different stages of progress. I think I'm just wired to enjoy having lots of stuff in the fire—learning new things and making progress with stuff that I care about. I don't know the word *boredom*. When I'm not working, I'm thinking about new projects I'd love to start. Some people dread Monday mornings and the start of a new workweek. Not me. I look forward to getting back to my office to bang some things out.

I know not everyone can say, "I love my job!" For those who work for a paycheck without a strong passion for the work, I don't think Parkinson's will change that. But maybe Parkinson's can help change your mindset, looking at things differently and becoming appreciative of certain parts of your job or other things that you are blessed with. Try to frame tasks as you "get" to do them versus you "have" to do them.

Take My Medication

I'm not a doctor, so I'm not going to share any medical advice except this: take the medication your doctor prescribes. After my diagnosis, I didn't start taking my medicine for a month. Looking back, I missed out on a month that I could have felt much better. In fact, I felt better almost immediately after I took my first dose.

When I first started taking my medication, I took one pill three times a day. Now, I take five different pills for a total of sixteen per day. I could get discouraged that I need more pills more often to keep my symptoms under control. But the truth is, I'm glad I can still move around and work as well as I can. I can tell the time of day by how my body feels, as the medication level drops off. I would be in bad shape if I didn't have this medicine to keep me moving.

As I write this, here are the medications I'm currently taking to control Parkinson's. These are just of few of the medications you might hear about from your doctor:

- Levodopa/carbidopa—to supplement my body with dopamine
- Entacapone—to make the dopamine not get absorbed into my system so quickly
- Amantadine—to try and control dyskinesias
- Rasagiline—taken as a possible neuroprotectant

There are many options for medication. You will learn that some medications treat the symptoms associated with Parkinson's, and others treat the symptoms caused by those medications. This leads me to the next point: become a student of your disease.

Learn About Parkinson's

Early on, I went to doctors and physical therapists to treat a frozen shoulder on my right side. It wasn't until I was properly diagnosed with young onset Parkinson's that I knew I had bradykinesia (slowness of movement) and rigidity (muscle stiffness), two symptoms of the disease. Occasionally, very light tremors (shaking) were present in my right hand, but since I'd always had a shake, that didn't stand out as a symptom until the doctors put all of the pieces together to form the diagnosis.

I mention the words like bradykinesia, rigidity, and dyskinesia because, while you might not know what they mean today, if you are on this journey, you will soon learn a new vocabulary. I urge those with Parkinson's to become students of the disease.

I've often said that I cannot imagine what it would have been like to have had Parkinson's fifty years ago. First, there were no treatment options or medications. People with Parkinson's had no options other than to be miserable. Second, there was almost no research.

Today, research exists on many fronts. For example, researchers have discovered—and now have genetic testing for—several Parkinson's genes: GBA, PARK7, SNCA, LRRK2, PARKIN, and PINK1. We're not quite there yet, but in the future, the genetic makeup of your Parkinson's may lead to more targeted treatment options.

The third reason I'm glad I didn't have Parkinson's fifty years ago is that we now have a ton of information at our fingertips via the internet. You can learn as much as you feel comfortable knowing about Parkinson's disease. If you or a loved one is tech-savvy enough, you can sign up for Google alerts to get notifications about anything new related to the disease and its treatment.

None of what I researched told me that this was a wonderful disease. But it did make me grateful that I was diagnosed early enough that I could find great relief from medication. Also, I learned about some of the things I could do to stay strong and mobile for as long as possible.

The only caveat I would add about doing research is to *know yourself*. Some people may become more fearful, anxious, and depressed as they study Parkinson's. Be honest with yourself. If you know that you are susceptible to getting overwhelmed when reading about a disease, have a loved one do the research for you so they can provide an overview. At the beginning of my journey, I needed my wife, Jennifer, to do the research. I was just too overwhelmed. Eventually, we both realized that I couldn't avoid taking charge of my health forever.

Get Involved in Parkinson's Research

I got involved in research studies, figuring if the results didn't help me, at least they might help someone further down the road who receives the same diagnosis. I joined 23andMe's Parkinson's project, the PPMI study, and Fox Insight.

23andMe was one of the first companies to offer personal DNA analysis. They realized at some point they could help disease research. One of the first studies they did was for Parkinson's; they asked participants to allow them to use their DNA to aggregate, study, and license to drug companies for research. I agreed to this.

Another research project was the PPMI study. I gave them a DNA sample to analyze. I'm a big fan of any group that can use my DNA if it might help me or someone else.

Another interesting research study is by Fox Insight. Participants answer a series of survey questions every three months. Thousands of people complete these questionnaires. I also gave them permission to use my DNA sample to be matched with my survey data. They share some version of the data they collect with pharmaceutical companies to prioritize and research new treatment options.

Filling out the surveys forces me to think about what has happened with my Parkinson's in the last thirty to ninety days, which can be good and bad. It's great when things stayed the same or even improved, like with medication. It's more challenging, though, when I realize that some things have gotten worse, or when I am reminded of what might still come in my future.

Here's an idea of some of the questions on the survey:

1. *With respect to your Parkinson's disease, how would you compare yourself now compared with your last study visit?*
2. *What is the most burdensome problem for you due to your Parkinson's disease?*
3. *Due to having Parkinson's disease, in the last month have you had difficulty:*
4. *Getting around?*
5. *Dressing yourself?*
6. *In the last thirty days, due to your Parkinson's:*

7. *Have you felt depressed?*
8. *Felt difficulty communicating with other people properly?*
9. *Experienced muscle cramps or spasms?*
10. *Dribbled saliva during the day?*
11. *Had a change in ability to taste or smell?*
12. *Had trouble swallowing or choking on food or drinks?*
13. *Experienced nausea, vomiting, constipation?*

Complaining or feeling sorry for myself is not constructive, and it takes me to a bad place. But doing something that might be part of the solution, leading to better treatment options or even a cure, gives me hope.

As far as I'm concerned, any emotional discomfort that these questionnaires cause me is worth it if they lead to better treatment down the line. Consider how you can get involved too.

Change My Perspective

Hearing that I had Parkinson's broke my heart, but my perspective is always being challenged. I read that 60 percent of the world's population don't have indoor plumbing, and about 30 percent don't have access to safe drinking water.

As bad as it sounds, in some ways we can use comparisons to measure our success or suffering. If I were to compare my bank account with that of Jeff Bezos, I would consider myself poor; but if I compare myself to the nearly 10 percent of the world living in extreme poverty—like those making less than $2.00 each day—I'm wealthy beyond measure.

The same holds true with illness. Yes, I have young onset Parkinson's. But I don't have young onset Parkinson's in rural India or South America where fewer experts and treatment options are available. When I consider that right now someone is hearing a diagnosis of stage IV cancer and being told they better wrap up their affairs as they probably only have weeks to live, it puts my disease in perspective, and it humbles me.

Sometimes when I hear people complain and get bent out of shape about things like "that restaurant messed up my order," I think to myself: *Do you have running water at home? Do you have a roof over your head? Do you own a car or have a good job? Are you cancer-free today? Now imagine trading problems with people who say no to any of those questions.* Those kinds of questions remind me of how fortunate I am compared to so many other people, and how little I have to complain about in relative terms.

Since I can't change my diagnosis, I've had to find ways to live with it. I don't want to be defined as "Blake, the guy with Parkinson's." That's not how I see myself. Yes, I have the disease, but I'd rather spend the rest of my life being a great husband, father, friend, son, brother, colleague, business partner, and member of the community. Parkinson's can't take those things away from me unless I let it. By making a choice to "accept the things I cannot change," I've gotten to a better place.

Not every day is perfect, and I still struggle at times. But I don't waste time beating myself up, playing the victim, or staying down. I want to be remembered for how I lived, not what disease I had when I died.

"**You**

Need

To

Know

This..."

CHAPTER 10

THINGS I WISH I'D KNOWN AT THE BEGINNING

WHILE YOU CAN'T *UNRING* THE PARKINSON'S BELL, THERE are some things you can do to give yourself the best possible chance for getting great treatment and extending your mobility, in spite of the disease. In the years since I was first diagnosed, I've thought about the big and small things I wish someone had shared with me, either to guide my thinking or help me form an action plan. In no particular order, I'll share some thoughts in this chapter which I hope you'll find helpful.

TAKE SOME TIME TO LET THE SHOCK SUBSIDE

I've been there. You're in shock. You have no hope. You think your world has ended. Believe me, it hasn't. Don't panic. Things will get better and won't appear as dark as they are now.

Some people get over the perceived devastation quickly. For others, in the category I include myself, it takes longer. Take whatever time you need to just grieve. It's okay. Sometime in the future, you will look back on this early time as less traumatic than it appears today.

FIND THE BEST DOCTOR YOU CAN

The best doctor is one you are comfortable communicating with, one you know is knowledgeable about movement disorders—preferably one who is a movement disorder specialist, and one you feel has your best interests in mind. Just like doing business with someone, you must feel comfortable with the person treating you. As I've shared, I looked around a bit before I found a doctor who I was happy with. You might be limited with the available options, but try not to settle. Find someone who gives you the balance you need, is convenient to you, and seems trustworthy.

PICK A MEDICATION PATH

When I got diagnosed, there was a question about whether a younger person with the disease should start taking the gold standard of treatment, carbidopa/levodopa, or if they should instead take a newer class of medications called dopamine agonists. For some reason, this decision haunted me.

The dilemma was this: after taking carbidopa/levodopa for some time, most people develop involuntary movements (called dyskinesias) that usually manifest when the medication is at peak dose. Because of this side effect, some doctors recommended starting with dopamine agonists. The challenge with dopamine agonists, however, is that some patients develop poor impulse control as a side effect. When it came to recommendations, the doctors I spoke with were either in one camp or the other.

I obviously wanted to stall my high chance of getting dyskinesias for as long as possible. There was, however, one question I could never quite seem to get clarity on. For a person predisposed to get dyskinesias (after a certain time period of carbidopa/levodopa use), would that dyskinesias potentially start later if they could take a dopamine agonist first, before moving on to carbidopa/levodpa later? Or was the time-window of medication-indued dyskinesias more determined by disease progression regardless? My belief is that it happens regardless, and the "runway" of side effect-free carbidopa/levodpa use is not extended by starting with the agonists. And since I was already taking carbidopa/levodopa and it was working great, I chose not to take the agonists and stay the course.

On the subject of medicine, I also had a doctor give me this advice: *Take enough medicine to make you feel good. Don't try to take less medicine on the front end, worrying it will be a bad decision later.* Which medication or medications to take and at what dose and when routinely changes with Parkinson's. When you're told you must add a medication or increase the dose of an existing one, it can feel like defeat—like the Parkinson's is winning. I've adopted the mindset that *it is what it is.* I've come to expect changes going forward, and I'm going to take whatever medicines I need to feel good TODAY.

TAKE YOUR MEDICATIONS AS SOON AS POSSIBLE

This is something I didn't do. I waited almost a month after my prescriptions were given to me to start taking those medications. My advice is not to wait, because the better you feel, the faster you will overcome grief.

RESIST THE URGE TO GO DOWN THE RABBIT HOLE OF "WHAT CAUSED THIS?"

During this period, you might have the urge to focus on how you got Parkinson's. For me, I had quite a list of possibilities as I wondered how I might have caused my disease. I spent weeks thinking about it. *Was it the well water I grew up drinking? The pesticides I was around? The Diet Coke I drank? The heartburn medication I'd taken for a long time? The allergy shots I'd gotten for years?* And so on. There is no answer to this puzzle, and even if there was, it would not change your treatment regimen nor your diagnosis. My advice is to avoid this mental trap altogether. It's a waste of time and energy.

Listen to the Audio Version of *Lucky Man* by Michael J. Fox

Instead of going down the rabbit hole of trying to figure out what contributed to your disease, listen to Michael J. Fox read his book, *Lucky Man.* This was very soothing to me, and I would encourage everyone to listen to the audiobook version of him reading instead of just getting the printed copy as it is more impactful.

Surround Yourself with the Right Support

As I mentioned, I didn't tell many people for the first couple of years. I've since learned that I'm an oddball in that department. Even the people I spoke with at the young onset Parkinson's conference were perplexed that I hadn't told my family or friends right away. It's not that I didn't feel like I could, it's that I didn't want to, especially since I couldn't do so without breaking out in tears. I needed to be ready, and I was not.

We're all different, so it's not surprising that the amount of support we need or want might vary. Initially, my wife Jennifer was my shoulder to cry on. As I branched out and told more family and then friends, they too became a source of support and encouragement.

When you're comfortable, start talking to people. You'll quickly learn who offers support, versus those who make you more uncomfortable than if you'd said nothing.

DECIDE IF AND WHEN YOU WILL TELL OTHERS— AND WHO YOU WILL TELL

Closely tied to the point above, be intentional about how you reveal your condition to others. Other than a very rare, involuntary twitch and some symptoms that were more hidden, most people didn't know I had Parkinson's. Besides not being in a good place to talk about it, I needed time to process everything. I knew I had a period of time where I could go on outwardly as normal. I couldn't keep it hidden for long. Once I let people know, I couldn't take that information back. I wanted to take advantage of this finite time-window, so I chose to keep my diagnosis a secret until I was ready for my life to outwardly change.

I didn't know how being "out" would change things. *Would people want to talk about Parkinson's all the time? Would people look at me with pity? Would my business partners still want to do business with me and would they question my capability?*

If you are employed, you might wonder how your employer will react. For me, embracing that outward "normalcy" was helpful while I was still getting comfortable with my diagnosis.

Don't Be Afraid to Reach Out for Help

When you first hear those five little words, "you have young onset Parkinson's," you may feel like your world has fallen apart. I've been honest that I felt heartbroken. Some people don't have a great support network available. By support, I don't just mean friends. I mean folks who can offer emotional and psychological support. If you feel like you would benefit from a counselor, pursue it. The disease is bad enough without the depression that is often associated with the shock of a tough diagnosis, along with the symptom of Parkinson's itself. There are many counselors who specialize in grief counseling. And make no mistake about it, for many people, learning of this diagnosis will put you in a tailspin of grief.

Exercise

One of the only things known to be effective in helping slow down Parkinson's is exercise. Although I have been riding a stationary bike one or two times a week for years, exercise has always been something I've had to force myself to do. I hated it. I tried personal training a few times, but I stopped each time after a handful of sessions.

I knew once I got diagnosed that I needed to really get on the exercise train, so in addition to riding my stationary bike twice a week, I hired a personal trainer six months into my diagnosis. Since his dad had Parkinson's and he also taught Rock Steady Boxing classes, he was perfect for me. I've gone twice a week for years now. We do boxing, ladder agility exercises, balance work, and weights. Having Parkinson's feels like your body is under attack. Over time, Parkinson's tries to manualize processes that were once automatic. I believe if you do not keep using a particular function, you will slowly lose it. That's why we do many exercises with Parkinson's in mind—examples include box squats, which help you maintain getting up from a seated position in a chair, routines to keep balance, and compound exercises to involve the brain so it doesn't become rusty.

If I could stress one thing it would be to get on an exercise program right away. If you have the means, hire a personal trainer, preferably one that has some type of experience in Parkinson's, or at least one that is willing to take some direction from you on what you need. Also, make sure each workout is varied, so you do not get bored with it. If you aren't able to get a personal trainer, then you can do these yourself.

More information can be found in the 'Resources' section of this book. However you do it, try to work in a little exercise every day when you are not doing a main workout.

*I keep a jump rope in my office in case I want
to wake up my brain in the afternoon*

Build a Care Team and Regimen With What Works for You

For me, this includes my doctor and physical trainer, Zach. I also get massages two to three times a month from my massage therapist, Rhonda, so she is part of my team. I go to a business that does stretching once per week. I see Shane there, so Shane is part of my regimen and team. I find that this works for me currently. For some people, speech or occupational therapists might be part of that team. There are also different modalities that you might add to your regimen, which I know some derive benefit from. These may include meditation, acupuncture, counseling, and others.

BE PREPARED

Keep your pills for the day in a contact lens case. It's easy to carry and helps you remember what pills you've taken for the day and which ones you haven't.

Keep a few pills of each type in multiple locations. For me, this includes my office, my car, my briefcase, my luggage, and my emergency medicine bag (which I'll detail shortly). If you lose a pill or forget your medication one day at home, you'll have backups. Also, if you run out of one medication unexpectedly, you'll have a few spares you can take—giving you time to get a refill.

Consider using an app on your phone to alert you when it's time to take your medications, because they work best when taken on time, every time. I've listed the app I use in the 'Resources' section.

Now, let me describe the emergency medicine bag. Put three days' worth of pills—along with your prescription schedule and interactions list—in a bag in a cupboard where you live, and tell your family about it. This way, if you wind up non-communicative in a hospital, they can bring it, and your doctors will know what to do. At the time of this writing, you can get a free emergency kit if you live in the U.S. The details are in the 'Resources' section.

My emergency medicine and instructions kit

Along with what I've listed, put a card in your wallet saying you have Parkinson's. Just like the wallet card that read "I'm not drunk, I have Parkinson's," this could help prevent embarrassment or hassle should you get pulled over.

Create and maintain a Parkinson's timeline. Mine is very free-form. I have a Microsoft Word document I keep adding to. I list the date something changes, such as if I notice a new symptom, as well as when/how something has improved, any new medication I have started, or one I have stopped, etc. This is a good resource to have, because inevitably, you'll be asked for details or a date that something first happened.

I set up Google News Alerts to email me every so often about new Parkinson's news. This is a great way to stay current on the latest developments.

I also digitized my signature and handwriting so I can potentially use it in the event I lose it. If you sign legal documents, financial records, or even file taxes, having your signature in a digital format makes it easier to keep on top of your life.

They think of everything: a Parkinson's 'explainer' card for your purse or wallet

KEEP BUSY

This is self-explanatory, but if you focus your mind on something interesting, you'll have less time to get depressed.

Live for Today, and Stay Optimistic

Will I suffer down life's road? That thought scares me. I don't want to suffer. *How will I do with many years of Parkinson's under my belt? If someone is a certain way with twenty years of Parkinson's under their belt, will I be like that person when I am at the twenty-year point? What will I be like at my daughter's wedding? How long will I live? Will I get psychosis?*

I've struggled to get over my guilt for what I was doing to my wife, Jennifer. I've never wanted to be a burden to her. I know my needs will increase over time, and she never signed up for this.

These thoughts are not only unhelpful, but they are also untrue. For example, let me share my wife's response about me "being a burden." I wrote this book without telling her. I wanted to surprise her with it, and I asked her to be the first one to read it. When she read what I wrote about being a burden, she made a note in the margin that means more to me than gold:

> "You aren't a burden.
> You're a blessing in every way."

Don't allow yourself to get caught up in worry and fear about things that may never be. We don't know what tomorrow will bring.

Choose instead to look at the bright side of things and not overthink anything. I woke up this morning. The sun is shining, and it's going to be a great day. Although I'd rather not have Parkinson's, it's certainly not stage IV pancreatic cancer. Medical advancements are happening rapidly and exponentially, and better treatments are around the corner.

As painful as it was, my diagnosis was relieving in some ways. It tied all the strange things that had been happening together—like my shoulder issues, my foot twitching, and even things like Jennifer reading my sometimes lack of smile as me being mad at her. The diagnosis solved this whole puzzle.

I've even lost some weight, which had always given me high cholesterol readings. Those levels are now normal. I never would have lost that weight. Perhaps if I hadn't gotten Parkinson's, I would've died of a heart attack. I lovingly refer to it as the "PD Diet."

Now I'm more empathetic with those facing a medical condition. And I'm a more thankful person because of Parkinson's.

See the difference in mindset?

Look at Every Aggravation as an Opportunity for Your Health

I'm in the car ready to go, belted in, and someone asks me to get out of the car for whatever reason—say, to open a door. Even though I might be stiff, and getting back out of the car once I'm settled in is the last thing I want to do, I do it. I force myself into the mindset that getting in and out of the car as much as possible is good practice for maintaining function with my Parkinson's.

You might get aggravated if you drop some coins on the floor. You're a little stiff and do not feel like picking them up. Change your mindset and pick them up one by one, happily knowing *you're helping yourself maintain function*.

Asked to get out of that comfy chair at home in the evening, move boxes, or whatever task? Rather than get frustrated, try to frame it in your mind that *you're helping yourself maintain function*.

When tasks like buttoning become challenging, take the use-it-or-lose-it attitude of knowing *you're helping yourself by giving it a try*. Look at it as another form of a workout.

Again, your mindset has a lot to do with how your body will respond to little daily aggravations.

Do Little Things That Make You Feel Good

Do things that give you hope or that have a potential upside if they make sense, are not too burdensome, and have no or little downside. One probably silly-sounding thing I do is go around the house and sometimes outside barefoot. I'm always in socks, with or without shoes. I read that it is important to walk around barefoot from time to time to maintain sensations in your feet—the loss of which would impair balance. There is no downside to this, so I do it. When I go upstairs, I try to keep and improve my gait by going up two stairs at a time. When I'm standing up waiting for whatever reason, if I think about it, I'll lift a foot and hold it up for a bit to practice my balance. When I am driving by myself in the car, I will often sing at full volume to the music I am listening to so my voice stays strong. I randomly jump rope for 30 seconds for a burst of energy. I also practice walking backwards from time to time for coordination.

Never Lose Hope

They're making medical breakthroughs all the time. Do I expect a cure for my disease in my lifetime? I'm very hopeful. If not a cure, I wouldn't be at all surprised if they came up with a whole new series of medications that could slow my disease progression or offer me even better relief of my symptoms. They might even come up with a way of reversing the disease.

I've read about some procedures that people have had great results with. There's always hope, and I'm optimistic about Parkinson's discoveries during my lifetime. *As long as there is life, there's a reason to believe things can get better.* And that type of thinking certainly beats the alternative.

CHAPTER 11

QUOTES

I'VE ALWAYS WANTED TO WRITE A BOOK. However, I wanted to write a book on quotes that I found amusing. Believe me, a book on Parkinson's wasn't what I had in mind.

To keep in line with my first goal, I thought I'd share a few of my favorite quotes here in regard to Parkinson's in the hopes they are of help to you.

"There's the *right now* and the *not right now*. Don't let the *not right now* get in the way of the *right now*."

One of my best friends, Bill, shared this quote with me not long ago. It's really a life philosophy, but it applies directly to Parkinson's. If your brain is like mine and tends to run fifty steps ahead, you churn out never-ending data sets of *what-if* questions and unhelpful future thoughts. With Parkinson's, those thoughts are ones like: *What if the medicine stops working? Will I have problems walking? When will I need brain surgery?*

When a thought pops into my mind, I ask myself, "Is this a *today thought* or a *future thought?*" Then I only entertain *today thoughts* and push the *future thoughts* until they come due. This has been extremely helpful to keep a lifetime of worries from hitting me at the same time. So I stay in today: *What medication should I take today? What can I do to feel better today? What fun or interesting things can I do today?*

"If you wake up in the morning, it's going to be a good day."

This is more about your attitude than anything else. We're all lucky to be alive. Try to be thankful that we "get" the privilege of being alive. Even if you face many obstacles, waking up is a treasure and privilege that many who are no longer here don't have.

"This is too important to squander."

My translation of this is that life is a gift, even with Parkinson's. Make every day count.

"Change your mindset, change your life."

In life, you get what you give. No matter what life topic we're talking about, rather than think of stuff you *have* to do, think of it as something you *get* to do. It will change who you are for the better. For example, I take my daughter to school every day. It takes about twenty minutes to drive each way. More challenging is getting up at 6:00 a.m. every school morning. Rather than looking at getting up that early as a chore, I look at it like it's a gift and honor to be able to take Eleanor to school each day—allowing us to have dedicated, special "our time" together in the car.

"Everybody gets kicked out of the box eventually."

We're all going to die. It's just a matter of when and from what. Like a band that falls out of favor only to return as a second act more popular than ever, just because you have Parkinson's doesn't mean you can't have your own second act or that your life is over.

"The irony is that on a cloudy day, there is sunshine above. You just have to find it."

When I fly, I love to look out the window. It's always amazing to me that even though it might be a truly dreary day, once you pop out above the clouds, there is bountiful sunshine above. We've been dealt some bad news. It's hard to move past it. Just know that even though your outlook is currently cloudy, that darkness is only temporary.

"Why focus on what you don't have when you can focus on what you do have?"

I think of this quote mainly as one for combating consumerism, but I also see it as a reminder to remain happy and content with your life. Be satisfied with the good things you have, versus always seeking something else. Count your current blessings.

"It does not matter how slowly you go, as long as you don't stop."

Keep your focus on moving ahead, even if it is a little bit at a time.

"Into each life some rain must fall."

— Henry Wadsworth Longfellow,
from "The Rainy Day"

No person's life is perfect. We all will have some challenges and obstacles to deal with. Expect the rain. But also expect that you will see the sun again.

"Every morning, you get to wake up and choose how you see the world."

If you think you're going to have a bad day, you will. If you think you're going to have a wonderful day, you will. You get to choose what kind of day you'll have.

"An idle mind is not good for anybody."

Don't let your mind keep torturing you with the diagnosis. Find something else to concentrate on and give your attention to.

"It's all a matter of perspective—do some camping, and then all of a sudden the Days Inn seems like the Four Seasons."

Sometimes we just need a reset. When I allow myself to grumble about having Parkinson's, I remind myself of the number of people that leave the doctor's office with a terminal diagnosis. Then I feel fortunate.

LIFE AFTER DIAGNOSIS

ONE YEAR LATER

SKI TRIP IN TELLURIDE,
COLORADO WITH
JENNIFER AND ELEANOR

CONSTRUCTION AT
OUR HOUSE:
LETTING ELEANOR
DRIVE THE BOBCAT

OUR BLACK LAB, ROGER

THE THREE OF US AT
A HOT SPRINGS
IN COLORADO

ELEANOR AND I IN
TELLURIDE, COLORADO

NEW YORK CITY DONUT SHOP

THREE YEARS LATER

SKIING WITH TWO
OF MY BEST FRIENDS,
TRIPP AND BRYCE

IMPORTING DIET COKE INTO THE PEPSI
HOTEL (OK, MAYBE I HAVE A PROBLEM...)

ELEANOR AND I AT THE
ST. PATRICK'S DAY FESTIVAL

Backstage at the beach boys concert

Vero Beach

Five Years Later

FAMILY DINNER IN
NEW YORK CITY

Six Years Later

CONEY
ISLAND
HAUNTED
HOUSE

JENNIFER AND I AT
ELEANOR'S 13TH
BIRTHDAY PARTY

SEVEN YEARS LATER

SEVEN YEARS LATER (AND TWENTY
POUNDS LIGHTER), THE GREAT
SILVER LINING OF MY PARKINSON'S
DIAGNOSIS: I CAN FINALLY EAT
WHATEVER I WANT!

SUPPORT

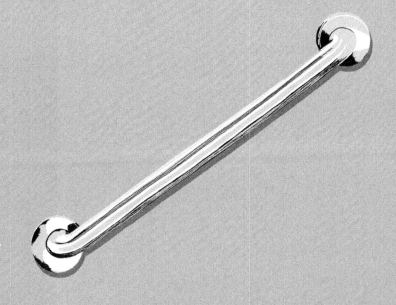

RESOURCES

When I was first diagnosed with young onset Parkinson's, the only person I knew with the disease was Michael J Fox. And of course, I didn't know him as much as I knew about him and his diagnosis.

Within the first year of my own diagnosis, I went to a couple of conferences focused on the disease, interviewed multiple doctors, signed up for studies, offered up my DNA in hopes it would lead to better treatment, and spent hours and hours educating myself.

I wrote this book to offer hope to others who have received a similar diagnosis, as well as for those who love them. I'm not a subject-matter expert on Parkinson's, but I feel fortunate enough to have talked to and learned from some of the top researchers and experts in the field. To help you as you learn more about this disease, I want to share a list of resources that I've personally used and would recommend to others. So if you don't see an organization listed, I didn't intend that as a slight.

Following are the organizations, opportunities, and activities I highly recommend:

NOTABLE ORGANIZATIONS

Michael J. Fox Foundation
www.michaeljfox.org

National Parkinson's Foundation
www.parkinson.org

American Parkinson's Disease Association
www.apdaparkinson.org

Davis Phinney Foundation
davisphinneyfoundation.org

EXERCISE OPTIONS

Rock Steady Boxing
www.rocksteadyboxing.org

PWR

www.pwr4life.org

LSVT Big/LSVT Loud

www.lsvtglobal.com/IdaIndexLSVT

Black Dog Fitness

www.blackdogfitness.com

Stretch Fusion

www.stretchfusion.com

RESEARCH PARTICIPATION OPPORTUNITIES

Fox Trial Finder

www.michaeljfox.org/trial-finder

ClinicalTrials.gov

www.clinicaltrials.org

CONFERENCES

World Parkinson's Congress

www.worldpdcoalition.org

International Congress of Parkinson's Disease and Movement Disorders

www.mdscongress.org

COMMUNITIES

MJF Buddy Network

parkinsonsbuddynetwork.michaeljfox.org

OTHER RESOURCES

My Medication Diary

apps.apple.com/us/app/my-medication-diary/id947796077

Parkinson's Hospital Kit

www.parkinson.org/Living-with-Parkinsons/Resources-and-Support/Hospital-Kit

Google News Alerts

www.google.com/alerts

POSITIVE MESSAGING

Joel Osteen

www.joelosteen.com/how-to-watch/podcasts

***Seven Years Later: Blake with original signed photograph
of Mohammed Ali, long before they shared a Parkinson's
diagnosis (or boxing!)***

About the Author

A serial entrepreneur since childhood, Blake sold T-shirts at the family restaurant before investing in a jukebox as his first "turnkey" operation. Work and pleasure have taken Blake to many places, introducing him to many people. On any given day, you can find Blake having fun—working, brainstorming new ideas, and spending time with his family.

Refusing to be defined by Parkinson's, Blake continues to live his best life in Knoxville, Tennessee with his wife, Jennifer, their daughter, Eleanor, and their black lab, Roger.

For more information about Blake and this book as well as a regularly updated list of further resources, please visit:

www.YoungOnsetParkinsonsDisease.com

Printed in Great Britain
by Amazon

29201028R00111